The House in Rock Park

~~~~~~

'Joni Munnerly'
~~~~~~

This is a work of fiction. Events and characters described are not based on real incidents nor on any person now living or dead.

First Published 2009 by Word WEAvers

British Library Cataloguing in Publication Data.
A catalogue record for this book is available from the British Library.

ISBN 978 0 9541026 2 3

Acknowledgements

The Munnerlys were a larger than life family and it has taken a group of writers to research their world and tell their history. 'Joni Munnerly' therefore has to thank the following for writing each of their stories:

Louise Binns for	James Bartholomew
Cy Ferguson for	Edward
Joanna Graham for	Annie Smith
George Horsman for	Margery and Peter
Judy Hughes for	Florence
Andrew Kay for	George
Sue Ogonovsky for	Tom
Lynne Quarrell for	Amos, Arthur and Joni
Fae Turner for	Henry

Some additional material by the editor Gee Williams
'ego autem coacervavi omne quod inveni'

Images on pages 20, 56, 74 and 100 by permission of CreativeCommons
Cover 'Sailing ship' by Vivienne Blakeman. All other photographs, artwork and book design by D.A.Williams

In memory of Joe Colton and John Getty

CHAPTER 1

I should have known better than to go to that reception, but I suppose some part of me craved attention – even though there was a time when I'd had more than I wanted. As the daughter of the author Peter Munnerly, and descendent of that once-great merchant family, when I was caught touring the Middle East with a troupe of exotic dancers a few years ago it had caused- well, something of a stir. The clan had been furious, but that was the whole point, of course.

It had begun with a request: would I give or lend the portrait of my ancestors, George Munnerly and co, to be included in a Prominent Liverpool Families exhibition? I agreed. It was one of those City of Culture 2008 events. My invitation to the opening was in the nature of a 'thank you'. Unfortunately it was marred by the fact that my husband, Phil, flatly refused to come with me. Saying he'd pick me up afterwards wasn't the same thing. Clearly he thought the party would involve being pleasant to a number of pretentious idiots so I was likely to need a few drinks. Annoyingly he'd been right. I was on my third glass of unimpressive red wine and they were still working through the speeches.

'Grim looking bunch.' The soft voice, with a hint of Ireland in it, broke into my thoughts and I turned to view the speaker. Tall. About forty. Attractive in a gangly, unkempt way. Artist? Someone from the media? Time was when I'd have wanted to find out more but all that nonsense was nearly a decade in the past.

'Sorry?'

He jerked his head towards a picture. My picture as it happens. 'This lot. Sinister looking buggers.'

It wasn't a bad description. They were handsome people but nothing could entirely soften those dark, arrogant faces. Of the fourteen people in the picture only young Henry and Helena showed something of that generosity of spirit that cropped up occasionally - like a sport - in the Munnerly line. I hated the damned thing. Havana House, the ancestral pile, was a pretty depressing place even without having the lot of them looking over your shoulder. Obviously this bloke was unaware of my family connection.

'A bit harsh,' I suggested out of cussedness.

His smile was engaging. 'I wouldn't want to mess with them.'

'Me neither.' I took another sip of my wine. In the background a full orchestral version of *Yesterday* filled the pause, all strings and schmaltz. I had nothing else I wanted to add.

'What a tribe!' He seemed determined to motor on. I could see him counting the figures. 'Nine girls and one boy. God! I wonder what happened to them all.'

I pointed to one of the girls. 'Alice tried her hand at art.'

'Don't recall an Alice Munnerly.'

'She was married by then. Never had much success though. Popular taste was for pretty landscapes and still life. Alice wanted to paint gritty realism. Not acceptable, from a woman especially.'

'Ahead of her time.'

'You could say that.' I pointed to another female amongst the multitude. 'That one was involved in social welfare. The rest just got married and produced babies for the Empire.'

'And the boy inherited the business?'

'Yeah, but he preferred seafaring to management.'

The suspicion dawned on his face as he squinted at the labeling next to that massive ornate frame. 'Oh my God - I get it. You're Joni! The last of the Munnerlys.'

I shook my head. 'My father was the last of the Munnerlys. The name is extinct.'

It took just a moment for the implication of this to be digested. 'Er - you'd have thought that there'd be loads of descendents with all that lot.'

'Too few boys, too many wars and some very bad habits.'

To give him credit he recovered well. 'I shouldn't have been so rude about them. As a matter of fact I used to be quite a fan of your father's books. I remember reading Burlington and The Beast of Beng -'

I raised an eyebrow in disbelief. 'How old were you? Ten?.'

He grinned. 'You're not an admirer?'

'God no! How could anybody take that cut price Bulldog Drummond rubbish seriously?'

'Still, there's a lot of interest in your father's work again. Especially after what happened to him- I mean... Do you think his stories were wish-fulfillment? Was Burlington his alter ego?'

That hit another nerve. I had often thought that Dad's more dangerous extravagancies had been prompted by his own creation. The bloke must have seen that I was uncomfortable and changed the subject.

'A top up?' He drained his glass.

'I shouldn't.'

'Driving?'

'Calories.' I watched him run an eye over my best tailored blue suit.

'You don't look like you have to worry. More wine?'

'Thanks.'

'I'm Chris Harrington by the way.'

He disappeared into the elegantly dressed scrum around the refreshment table and returned with the drinks and 'nibbles.' By the time we'd finished the tiger prawns in tempura, I'd found out that he represented a Dublin publishing house. George Munnerly's Irish origins were an obvious point of interest. And somewhere during the conversation - somehow - he convinced me to have a go at writing an account of the life and times of the Munnerlys. When I told Phil he said I wasn't fit to be let out on my own but looking back I don't regret it.

Not everything I found out was good but everybody likes to know where they come from. I'm no exception.

.

The family records, so jealously guarded by Great Aunt Flo, had been stowed in a garage when they came into my father's possession. I had treated them little better. Now I moved the various boxes into the study of the neat, modern house Phil and I shared in Bebington on the Wirral. Not all that far away in distance, perhaps, but a world away from the Munnerly's old fortress, Havana House in Rock Park.

There was a huge volume of paperwork - an enormous, unsorted amount that almost extinguished my enthusiasm before I got started. Perhaps it was Phil's scorn for the project drove me on. To make a start I disciplined myself to read nothing, rather to consider how best the material could be organized. The obvious choice would be a chronological system but that meant that documents relating to different individuals would overlap. Confusing. Equally, some material might concern more than one person. My eventual solution was to put all the documents relating to each of my ancestors into a separate stacker box, having copied items as necessary, together with any relevant personal effects. I then undertook a preliminary examination of all that I had. In the end I decided to limit myself to writing about those in the direct line of descent, because George and Rosina's descendents rivaled those of Queen Victoria in number and spanned all the continents of the world. But none of the dispersed bore the name of Munnerly.

So my intention was to start with old George himself. But the picture – long despised - now caught my imagination. It really was a remarkable piece- if not of art then at least of social documentary. I visited it once, twice... infuriating to think that now I wanted to study the thing I had to cross the Mersey each time, when for years it had been there as an unacknowledged backdrop to my past. Among the accounts, reports and deeds I found letters between George and a Mr. Rimmer who was acting on behalf of the poor artist commissioned to execute the great work. From there I found the artist himself.

James Bartholomew was born in 1854 into a family of Cheshire landowners but left home in his early twenties to study at the Liverpool School of Art. He enjoyed limited success as a portrait artist in the city in the 1880s. He developed an interest in landscapes and, particularly, seascapes when he moved to the North Wales coast, where he lived from 1919 until his death from old age in 1941. The Munnerly Portrait is the only surviving example of his work as a professional portrait painter, this art being overtaken by the new fashion for photography which James himself eventually adopted in order to maintain a living.

He married the daughter of a local publican in 1890 and his photographic studio, the Bartholomew Gallery, was established above the bar of The Mariners public house in the same year. The studio was taken over by his son after the Great War.

In 1975, when The Mariners was cleared for the pub's refurbishment as a restaurant, several previously unseen paintings by Bartholomew came to light - notably a study of an unidentified, dark-haired young woman in late Victorian dress. This small oil is currently on permanent loan to the Walker Art Gallery and the other paintings were on display in the restaurant's main dining room until the early 1980s when they were lost during a further redevelopment.

Poor James Bartholomew. It was typical of George to want a bargain but his method of negotiation was unsubtle to say the least.

Had he been as ruthless, as overbearing, to the young painter in person...?

The Painting

A thin grey light penetrated the fabric draped across the window and the furniture threw dark shapes against the encroaching October morning. James Bartholomew shaded his eyes with his elbow and groaned. They had buried William Daniels "the Rembrandt of Liverpool" the previous day and his friends had paid tribute to him by visiting his favourite public houses, including those whose signs he had painted, singing and arguing as if William himself had been amongst them. James had found his way home in the early hours of the morning and, he groaned again at the memory, banged on the door of his lodging house until he had gained entry. Gathering the bedcovers around his narrow frame he swung himself upright and leaned back against the wall with his eyes closed, allowing his legs to swing over the side of the bed, his toes tapping at the floor in search of his shoes. He took several deep breaths, sniffed and opened his eyes.

Across the room the dark mouth of the small iron fireplace gaped back and he saw that his clothes lay where they had fallen as he had exchanged them hastily for the bedcovers. He lifted both arms and surveyed the backs of his hands, pale as chalk in the half light. They were not trembling, which was good, but still aching and stiff - each joint protesting as he flexed his fingers in and out of fists. Even in this gloom he could see the dark ink and paint stains that marked him as an artist.

In this part of Liverpool that was not unusual – he had sought lodgings on Brownlow Hill because it was where the city's growing school of artists and sculptors had chosen to dwell. He had been fortunate to secure the use of a studio close by and he greatly appreciated the company of others who shared his passion. He was also hopeful that his work might be thought promising by the visiting patrons and academics, keen to promote the artistic life of Liverpool now that economic prosperity had secured its commercial future. And he himself, James Bartholomew, had just secured a commission to paint one of the city's most successful merchants, George Munnerly.

Ambition warmed his body sufficiently to rise and cross the room to splash his face in the bowl set for that purpose in the corner. The Munnerly commission had been a surprise but he had accepted it eagerly even though he had not yet met the man himself but only his agent, Mr. Rimmer. He had stressed the great advantage that James might gain if his painting was a success, for all of Liverpool Society knew Mr. Munnerly and many fine parties were held in Havana House, where the painting might hang if it met with his approval.

James knew that he could make his name with a portrait and it was indeed a lucrative line of work, given the number of successful merchants and leaders of civic society now celebrating the fruits of their labours with conspicuous and lasting displays of wealth. This circle of patrons and prospective customers would likely see his work and other commissions would follow. God willing, he would be able to pursue his vocation as an artist without fear that he would have to return to his family and admit defeat. But it would all be in vain if he were late, he thought, and dressing at great speed, James took his sketching book and pencils and hurried out of his room for his appointment with Mr. Munnerly at Havana House.

The ferry crossing from the Pier Head to Woodside helped to clear his head - a stiff breeze whipped down the Mersey and seagulls were wheeling and calling across a grey sky. He shivered. The gulls were an aspect of life by the sea that he did not care for - their mournful cry always lowered his spirits. However the noise and vibration of the paddle steamer's engines, and the slap of the waves against the side as they berthed, all served to drown the birds' calls. He gathered his collar around his throat and set his head purposefully against the wind as he stepped onto the landing stage and made his way under the covered walkway to the shore. James had never been to Rock Ferry before and he was surprised by the style and number of large houses along the Chester Road. He had seen several leafy spaces as he made his way to the address, following Mr. Rimmer's instructions. "Do not, under any circumstances, arrive late or you will certainly regret it," he had cautioned. What manner of man was he about to encounter? He had heard that the merchants and ship-owners were hard men who had fought their way to prominence. Although there were certainly cultured professionals in the city and landed gentry nearby, the merchant class was altogether a different kettle of fish. But he was himself - was from a good family with some minor aristocracy on his mother's side. She would certainly not approve of this commission - he grimaced at the thought of her reaction. Well, seeking patronage was the fate of the artist and he would not concern himself with how the money had been made - that was the attitude of a different era.

He lifted his head and, looking across the road, realised that he was at his destination, Rock Park, and that there before him - an imposing corner mansion, surrounded by railings and with an impressive front portico - was Havana House. James checked his pocket watch - he was in fact a few minutes early. Crossing the road with care he stopped outside the house and looked up. A lace curtain fell back from a window on the first floor. He was being watched! He approached the porch and then stopped. Would he be welcome at the front door? Perhaps better not to suffer the humiliation of being refused entry there. Looking around he saw a sign affixed to the railing - Tradesmen - with an arrow painted in black pointing to the left and then to the back. He walked to the corner and descended the stone steps to the kitchen door. His arrival there caused some consternation and he was left waiting outside while Mr. Rimmer was fetched to escort him through the house. Mr. Rimmer's broad shoulders led him through the back of the building and at such speed that he had only a fleeting impression of a substantial kitchen and parlour and a great deal of bustle and clatter. They climbed a wooden stair and hurried down a dark panelled corridor into the light and calm of a galleried entrance hall, a great oak staircase winding up to the first floor.

"In here," said Mr. Rimmer, opening doors to the left side, which James saw led into an elegant sitting room. "I will tell the family that you have arrived. Please wait." The doors closed with a thud, leaving James to survey the room. The scent of lilies from a large vase made his head swim and he tried not to breathe too deeply. Morning light only just filtered through lace curtains hung between heavy velvet drapes and he was struck by how richly the furniture shone, the glossy surfaces glowing with colour… but the sound of footsteps prevented further inquiry into bookcases and cabinets. A humming resolved itself into female voices, chattering like birds, getting louder as he turned towards the doors and then, as he stiffened, moving away from the room he was in and receding again. He stared at the double doors, willing himself to see what lay beyond, but the polished oak merely reflected his own frame. Now he heard briskly approaching steps and one of the doors did open inwards. Mr. Rimmer beckoned him into the hall. They crossed towards another gleaming doorway, with a large shiny-leaved tropical plant on a pedestal to one side, and now he realised here had been the destination of all that feminine prattle. Mr. Rimmer strode forward.

"Mr. James Bartholomew." he announced and James stepped into the silence that fell at that instant. His first impression was of a room full of identical women, each with curled hair and wearing a high-necked dress, the crisp white cotton frills contrasting with the honey complexion and dark eyes. They were all gazing at him with the same haughty expressions and his skin burned under his clothes. He looked for Mr. Rimmer to make the necessary introductions but the group of women parted and a dark figure strode to the front.

"So, you are the artist!" George Munnerly's tone was hearty but mocking and James thought he would melt with embarrassment. "Rimmer said you were young and, by God, he was not wrong. I hope you know your craft, eh?"

"Yes, yes, I showed Mr. Rimmer some examples, I have done a number of portraits, some fellow artists, and, of course, self-portraits, but also members of my family and other acquaintances, and, er, students and models for my studies at the Liverpool School of Art." He stopped suddenly and swallowed. Mr. Munnerly was eyeing him severely.

"Well, only the best will do for my family so I expect you to make your mark, young Bartholomew, and paint something I can be proud of. What do you have in mind?"

James searched the room, as if for inspiration. It was an elegant library, the same glowing woodwork as the sitting room, with several low chairs and desks and bookshelves packed with bound volumes. Paintings of ships in gilt frames filled the spaces between the shelving and lamps augmented the lace-shrouded natural light. He looked back at Mr. Munnerly, his mind whirring.

"Um, I had thought, something... something showing you surrounded by symbols of your business... nautical symbols and maritime images, images from your life in trade..."

Munnerly gazed fixedly at the younger man, whose stomach turned over with nerves. "I want something classical - Greek or Roman or such-like - something educated that will endure for posterity, a good painting of the highest quality showing me and my family at the height of our powers."

"Yes, of course, Mr. Munnerly. Er, how many family members did you have in mind for inclusion, may I ask?"

"All of them, of course. Why else do you think they are congregated here like a Sunday choir? You will include myself, my son Amos, his wife and his family, and of course Rosina, Mrs. Munnerly, the mistress of this house."

He waved his arm back towards the women who had separated into groups, revealing beyond them an elderly lady in a chair and a red-faced, corpulent man in his fifties alongside a slight lady of around the same age. As he looked, James realised that there was also a boy seated near the fireplace. The young women were all of different heights - different ages he realised. It was an enormous group for a family painting.

"It, um, it will be a big painting, Mr. Munnerly. A large canvas, with, uh, you and Mrs. Munnerly at the centre, yes, I think at the centre with Mr. Amos Munnerly and Mrs. Amos

Munnerly behind and then the young ladies, as a group of er…" he tried desperately to count them, his lips moving.

"Nine, man. I have nine grand-daughters and, eventually, one grandson."

"Nine. So, they could represent, erm… the Nine Muses!" He realised he had almost shouted it out with relief. "Yes. The Nine Muses, that could work, that could work." He caught George Munnerly's non-committal expression - the man was observing him, not altogether benignly.

"Muses, eh? Well, as long as it's classical, mind. Now, what do you want from us today?"

James made individual pen portraits of the family during the morning in the library, to fix them in his memory. He had arranged them approximately into the group he had drawn in his mind, but it had been almost impossible to keep their attention and he had hesitated to raise his voice. Mr. Munnerly had shouted instructions when the chattering rose to a high pitch, but James suspected that he had enjoyed his discomfiture. Mrs. Rosina Munnerly had said very little, remaining in her chair but watching the proceedings with the same intense gaze she had passed down through her family. Although quiet, particularly compared with the noise and bluster of her husband, hers was a strong presence and James hoped he could convey that somehow in his picture.

On his return to his lodgings he spread the sketches around his room. He knew there were nine Muses but he would have to check exactly what symbols he could use for each one. He was still struggling to work out how he could include them all and please his patron. The girls could be *made* to look lovely, but Mr. and Mrs. Munnerly senior were a glowering presence and as for Amos Munnerly and his pallid wife, Joan… Amos had spent most of the morning pouring glasses of sherry from the sideboard next to the bookcases and muttering to his wife. His ruddy complexion would have to be moderated for the portrait and, combined with his straining waistcoat and pendulous watch and chain, the total effect was of a grotesque Flemish character, not a classical figure at all.

James sighed. He needed a glass of ale himself and he decided that he would go and consult with his fellow artists in one of their favourite meeting places. If nothing else, he needed to commission a large canvas to be cut and stretched on a frame. It would be hard work taking it to and from the house on the ferry and he had no idea how he was going to manage. In the event, as soon as James had purchased the blank canvas and carried it to Havana House, George Munnerly had not allowed it to leave. It had been placed on his easel at the lightest end of the library and when James had made as if to take it with him, George Munnerly had stopped him.

"You're not taking a half-finished picture of me out onto the street, for ridicule. No, the painting stays and you come and work on it here."

This had made James's life easier in some senses, but also meant that he was under the household's eye much more than he might have liked. He had started to enjoy the ferry crossings, carrying his colour box, brushes and palette under his arm. He left his lodgings early and returned late. Relaxation in that grand library was impossible and he ate the sandwiches and ale he was brought by the housekeeper as quickly as possible. But… working in the house did mean that he could arrange for family members to pose for him and once he moved from pencils to paints he had to admit that he was pleased at how the painting was taking shape and he began to feel more confident. He had identified the correct symbols for the muses and he imagined the Munnerly girls appearing as a host of dark-curled angels whose pale faces shone from behind a god-like, imposing couple - Zeus and Hera perhaps - and he smiled at his own wit. The classical allegory did not stretch to their attire, however, and he struggled to overcome the effect of the high-necked formality of their dress, ultimately succeeding by highlighting the light and brightness of their youthful skin and shining eyes which stood out against the darkness and constraints of their clothing. The sisters for the most part ignored him, standing in small groups with an air of indifference or chattering amongst themselves, depending on their mood, with the exception of only the eldest and the youngest. Although she resembled her haughty sisters, Alice Munnerly, at twenty-one already a woman, observed him at work with a grave expression. On one occasion, when she had sat for him alone, he had been forced to ask her not to concentrate so hard on what he was doing, as she was craning her neck and frowning in a way he did not want to capture. She had blushed and apologised, which made him do the same, their joint confusion and embarrassment rendering both of them silent for the rest of that particular morning until she took him by surprise with a request. "May I view the canvas, Mr. Bartholomew?"

James was disturbed by the request - usually the daughters fled the room when released and although he knew that in his absence overnight someone was lifting the protective cloth and replacing it differently, he had attempted to avoid scrutiny of his work in his presence. "Yes, certainly, if you wish, please do." He stepped away from his easel and to one side. Alice placed herself some distance back from the canvas and remained very still as her gaze moved across his work, her eyelids flickering as she did so. James permitted himself to stare at her side profile whilst she was thus distracted and she turned suddenly to him, tipping her head back and raising her eyebrows as she spoke.

"Did you always want to paint?"

"Yes, yes, I believe I did, at least once I had discovered that such a life was possible."

She nodded, gave the canvas a last glance and strode towards and through the door, leaving him to examine the unfinished painting and attempt to divine her interpretation.

Helena Munnerly, at ten the youngest daughter, was sweet-natured and had a gentle smile which soothed James's taut nerves. She lacked the composure and self-conscious formality of the older sisters towards him and he thought it sad to contemplate how she would learn to suppress her natural warmth and grace. He tried to capture her spirit as far as he dared - her youth giving him license to show her gazing outward from the canvas with a smiling expression, something he could not attempt with the older girls without making them appear bold. The child was his only source of information about the household but he never had the chance to ask her any questions for she was always accompanied by one or more of the other girls who would invariably tell her to be quiet. He had to content himself with the snippets of information she would suddenly blurt out, including two particularly memorable statements. The first, which induced a mixture of shushing and giggling from the accompanying sisters, was that "Papa says that he will be glad when this vain charade is over… but it isn't really a charade is it, because we aren't pretending to be anything, are we, I mean not like real charades?"

James tried to hold his face without expression and continued to daub paint onto the same spot on the canvas, until he trusted himself to look again at his sitters. The second statement quickened his interest but, again, he felt compelled to conceal his reaction, the strength of which surprised him.

"Alice paints. She paints all the time, mostly flowers and fruits, but she says not half as well as you." Startled he stared at her but her chaperone for that day made a low remark of admonition and she flushed and looked down. He resumed his work but he felt a surge of pleasure at the compliment.

The boy, little Henry - the long-awaited heir - was also pleasant enough, although quickly bored. James placed him to one side in the foreground of the picture, his sex and singularity affording him special treatment. James found himself considering the boy's future as he worked. He had been educated in the style and manners of society and perhaps the family's wealth would release him from the shackles of his origins in trade. His grandparents were unlikely to live to see him far into adulthood and his father did not look to be in good health. If the sisters married well he would benefit and could expect to lead a comfortable existence, insulated from the efforts of his grandparents to create the wealth that was on such ostentatious display in the house... then he chided himself for the narrowness of his perspective - his artistic spirit and liberal attitudes had been dampened by the suffocating and contemptuous atmosphere of this household - and he found himself drawing on the confidence of his upbringing and family in quiet self-defence. His mother would be very satisfied, he thought with resignation.

James had not yet fathomed the matriarch of this family, Mrs. Rosina Munnerly. She had sat for him without protest but she settled herself in her chair and then regarded him with one eyebrow raised in an expression that he was loathe to replicate on canvas, so fearful it made him - it was all he could do to steady his hand as he applied the paint. She never spoke to him and his few instructions were complied with without acknowledgement. Surely Queen Victoria herself could not be more regal and intimidating a subject! He had also struggled with the positioning of Amos and Joan but finally settled for shades of the older couple, lacking the force and intensity of their presence. Amos made no secret of his contempt for the painting away from his father and Joan was a silent but nervous presence, no doubt worn thin by the demands of her large family and the strain of living in such a household.

No one could accuse him of not striving to make a flattering portrait of his patron, replacing Mr. Munnerly's habitual saturnine expression for one of pride and respectable solidity. He placed him amongst an ethereal cloud of young women and presented Rosina Munnerly as a figure of wisdom surrounded by the youth and promise of future generations.

The classical theme was enhanced by a background landscape in the Renaissance style, incorporating a distant view of a great river with ships heading out to sea, doubtless towards foreign shores. Yet he could not completely eradicate the dark cloud he felt embraced this family. As the painting progressed James was troubled by dreams in which George Munnerly appeared cloven-hoofed and hairy, an ancient leering satyr surrounded by sacrificial maidens. In one particularly vivid imagining, a red-faced and tormented Amos raged and postured, his wraith of a wife looking on with an anguished expression and the assembled girls a host of vengeful angels, dark and terrifying.

More than once, James had awoken gasping and drenched from the shock of gazing into the black centre of this alternate vision he had created in his own mind, and he wondered at the potency of the effect on him of this man and his family. He thought that he would be glad to complete his commission, for it troubled him to be so deeply affected. He considered himself too well-educated to be superstitious but he also took pride in his artistic sensibility and he feared that these images were dark portents for the family's future.

The decision that the painting was completed was taken not by James but by George Munnerly. James would have liked more time to work on certain points of detail that troubled him- the suggestion of a sparkle in Alice's eyes, the shadow across her mother's brow- but Munnerly's impatience had become more evident by the day, until eventually he declared the work finished and asked James to return the following day for payment. There was to be an unveiling before the entire family. James was surprised at how much this decision affected him. Despite his nocturnal forebodings and the atmosphere of Havana House, he had come to enjoy working on his commission and the process of painting had absorbed him to the point that he no longer felt the same disapproval and dislike from his sitters. They in turn had perhaps softened towards him, with the girls in particular starting to enjoy the painting once their individual images had become evident. He supposed that they had little else to entertain them, although he had taken care not to be too familiar and sensed that he remained a source of amusement to the end, with the possible exception of Alice, his fellow artist.

The space for the painting was already chosen, he knew - a blank wall at the head of the stairs, framed by the carved galleries and illuminated from above. James had risen early to be at the house after breakfast and he paced before the easel at the foot of the stairs, his work covered by a draped cloth. He had not seen the family congregated in full since that first meeting but now they filled the hallway, quieter than usual, perhaps subdued by the finality of the occasion. George Munnerly kept them all waiting but finally he descended the staircase with Rosina Munnerly on his arm, and they approached the easel, George looking straight ahead and nodding, but not meeting James's eye. James bent towards the corner of the draped cloth and peeled it back over the canvas in a single movement, letting it drop behind. He had signed his work with pride, the composition had all the classical elements that might be expected and it had worked better than he could have hoped. The interplay of light and shade between the principals and the supporting figures lessened the impression of a large formal group and he had made the Misses Munnerly look as if they were dancing behind the patriarch and his wife and son, their upturned faces gleaming with light failing from above. The family murmured behind him as James waited for Munnerly's verdict, but he turned to his wife Rosina instead.

"Well, Mother. What think you of this?" Interesting that whenever George addressed his wife it was then and only then that a trace of Irish brogue softened the voice. James held his breath as the old woman glanced at the portrait and then looked away, waving her free hand in its general direction.

"It will do. It will do well enough."

They left him in the hall with the same haste with which they had assembled at their first meeting. He had hoped that perhaps one or other of the girls, the youngest Helena or Alice the painter, might linger to say goodbye to him but the life of the house swept them on to their next activity without a backwards glance; he was already forgotten. Rimmer paid him and bade him farewell in a friendly manner, no doubt relieved that his choice had been satisfactory after all. As James approached the ferry and the wind whipped around his head his mood lifted and he too felt the sense of a chapter closing and new possibilities to come. Likely he would never see the painting, nor the Munnerlys, again.

Who's to say that's not exactly how it was? I've seen the painting, read up on the artist. More importantly I am a Munnerly in all but name now.

Some things you just know.

The completion of the picture came only just in time. It took pride of place at a party held at Christmas 1880, an affair that was at least as much business as pleasure. By Easter George Munnerly was dead. His will skipped a generation. As it happened Amos would not live to need his money. Typically the old man made provision for his grandchildren by means of a trust- but whereas Henry received his inheritance on his twenty first birthday, the girls would never have control of their fortunes. For those who married (five of them did) it would form a sort of dowry but those who did not would remain dependant on their brother. It was an attitude which infuriated me and I wondered whether he was simply a product of his times or...

Portrait of an Unknown Lady by James Bartholomew

CHAPTER 2

The Trade

From the age of exploration exemplified by Drake and Raleigh, the trafficking of 'lesser' human beings thrived. *The Trade* was immensely profitable. It was, therefore, irresistible to people and institutions sufficiently lacking in principle to invest in hugely. Among those active in this respect were such 'unimpeachable' establishments as The National Gallery, Lloyds of London and The Bank of England. Neither Parliament nor the Monarchy were free from its taint. Aristocrats enhanced their estates on its proceeds. Further down the line ship-owners, councillors, merchants and professionals benefited handsomely.

The Trade was operationally simple. Goods produced cheaply in English factories were shipped from ports such as Liverpool to West Africa. There they were exchanged for slaves, herded by predatory tribal chiefs into depots along the Coast. Shipped across the Atlantic to the Caribbean, the slaves were sold on West Indian plantations. From the proceeds, sugar, coffee, cotton, cacao and rum were bought.

Set amid mosquito-infested swamps and lagoons in the coastal fringes of tropical rainforest, the West African slave-depots represented the worst in human degradation. Malaria and yellow fever further reduced slaves already weakened and demoralized by captivity. Hopeless as their condition then was, it was nothing to what they endured throughout the infamous Trans-Atlantic *Middle Passage.* There were countless 'useless carcasses' cast over the side.

To the credit of William Wilberforce and like-minded statesmen, the public conscience was finally awakened to the evil of *The Trade.* But its end was not immediate...

George

"And how will I know her, this paragon of virtue and eminent good sense?" George had asked his friend.

"Oh, you'll know Rosina," Gabriel had said.

When, in 1825, young George Munnerly left his home in the little town of Clontarf on Dublin Bay, he was not the first to go nor likely would he be the last. Early, the holy fathers had noted the bright spark of his intelligence and marked him down for the priesthood. His education had proceeded accordingly. It was not until his studies at Trinity College, Dublin, were well advanced that he discovered in himself a mind and a will of his own. Not for him the soutane and the snuff! Deep in that tall, athletic frame, frustration festered and a spirit of adventure which craved release. The motivation was not *entirely* his. He had among his friends one Gabriel O'Halloran. Gabe had a cousin older than himself. Baldwin was the name. Rosina Baldwin ran a shipping agency in Liverpool with her father, but he was aging now and in declining health. She needed help. Liverpool was not the New World perhaps, but it might be a new beginning. If George liked.... On consideration, George *did* like. So here he was now, through Gabriel's ministrations, in the middle of a raging Irish Sea, among a ragtag of steerage passengers and penned-up pigs and poultry on the unstable, windswept, rain-washed deck of the *Duhb Linn. Not the most auspicious of beginnings*, he thought, yearning for earth underfoot, but mostly, just now, for something to placate the grumbling protests of his empty stomach.

He had little in the way of worldly goods to carry ashore - as little as had his fellow-sufferers of the steerage deck as they descended the narrow gangway. Into the arms of waiting dear ones they fell and then away into the rat-runs of streets bordering the great city's waterfront. And George was left alone - alone with his bundle on the quayside under a forest of towering masts and swinging derricks, alone and alien amid cries and purposeful activity indifferent utterly to his presence, until.... A movement that by its lightness and brightness caught his eye. Weaving its way among stacked casks and crates and bales, skirting great drays with their monumentally patient Shires and Percherons, came a dogcart. It was pretty and neat-as was its driver. A toss of her dark curls and she halted the vehicle within a yard of his solitary figure.

"Mr. Munnerly, I presume," she said. "I'm Rosina Baldwin."

"George Munnerly. Your servant, ma'am." That doffing of headgear, that over-generous sweep of arm and up-turned lip - did these not just border upon....? But....

"Someone younger, I had thought," she said, coolly noting his height, his breadth and regularity of feature.

"And someone older, I," he returned with shameless gallantry.

"Mm," she said. A touch of the whip, a clicking of little hooves, a spinning of bright yellow wheels, and away they sped before he had time properly to gain and settle on his seat.

"Something to satisfy the inner man?" It was less a question than an intimation of intent.

The stateroom of *The Narwhal's Tusk* was large. Its ceiling, low and crossed by massive beams, was stained to sullen amber by tobacco smoke of ages. Through blue-grey hanging haze, when his eyes had grown accustomed, George both saw and heard its occupants, easy round their tables. The undertones were deep and resonant, the weather-beaten features strong. Hands clasping fragile-seeming glasses were large and capable. It puzzled George that in this place of male preponderance Rosina's presence went unmarked, except when now a hand was raised in friendly recognition or when solicitous enquiries were made after her father's health. Even gaunt Martha, at the bar, nodded amiably as they passed into a room that offered greater privacy.

"He thinks a lot of you," Rosina was saying as they awaited their meal. "Tells me how *clever* you are; how you carried off the prizes at school. But Mr. Munnerly, well George then, if you must – George, make no mistake, *I mean business.* My father and I together we…. But more of that some other time, perhaps. *Cleverness,* though - it leaves me cold. Prizes are one thing, sound judgment something else again. Men out there, captains and their like, are tough as they come. Wouldn't be where they are now if they weren't. But they're no fools, and they play straight. They command respect. You earn theirs - then maybe we'll get along, the two of us. Do we have an understanding?" George pledged hand and heart in compliance, before diving in upon his well-heaped dish.

"Would the young gentleman care to see the room?" Mrs. Kedge's boarding house, Jamaica Street, heart of Liverpool dockland, came just within bounds of respectability. The good woman strove to keep it so. Her scars of battle showed – in habitual severity of feature, tightly disciplined iron-grey hair, work-rough hands and Spartan dignity of dress.

"*My* gentlemen," she took pains to observe, "*never* trouble *no-one*. And *that's* the way it's meant to be. But the young gentleman, would he care to …?"

Well yes, he would, and taking stock of the bruised and bullied furniture, the threadbare carpeting and faded decoration;

but again of the anxious eyes and the scrupulous cleanliness George, terms agreed, declared himself well satisfied.

A mile away, in Brunswick Street, was Baldwin's Agency. Near the oldest of the docks it occupied one floor of a bleak, blind-windowed building. Nor did inside reassure. Trailing his new-found employer who, with gathered skirts, ascended a steep and narrow staircase, he entered a room in state of dusty decline. This was to be his place of work; here and at the docks. The latter, though, was what captivated him: its urgency, its pungent, maritime odours, its great ships, gently tugging at their creaking hawsers, eager, it might seem, for infinities of sea and sky, and far-distant lands. One day perhaps...

"Tomorrow, then," Rosina brought him back to now. "We've work enough ahead, you'll note," she said, and left him to walk 'home' alone, through the meaner streets of dockside Liverpool.

Women! Careful where to set his feet in the mud and slime, George could not tear his eyes from them – women dirt-ingrained, dishevelled and encumbered by seeming droves of large-eyed, listless, pallid, clinging children; women hopeless in the doorways of their insalubrious hovels, awaiting return of their men. Of the dark and noisome depths beyond those doors it troubled him to think! But Liverpool, magnet to the most impoverished was magnet also to the enterprising wealthy. No need to traverse four thousand ocean-miles - *here* was his New World. *Here,* amid the grime, the squalor and the teaming life, were fortunes made, and *here* would he seek his. I *mean business,* did Rosina say? *Well*, George echoed in the privacy of his mind, *that we both*!

It would not happen overnight, or come about by chance. An apprenticeship had begun, had he but realised, when his boot-tip touched the Liverpool landing, when he perceived, beneath apparent chaos, a powerful, rhythmic discipline. Then his nerves had tingled to the tune of that focussed industry.

And he foresaw a time when he would be a vital part of it, young, decisive, resolute, resourceful. He would bring to his self-appointed task that sense of purpose his former studies had lacked. All Rosina asked of him he'd perform – and go far beyond.

Of ships, arrivals and departures; of sails and spars and times and tides; of cargoes and capacities and proper stowage; of destinations and documentation, the young scholar from Clontarf had everything to learn. But his will was strong, his sources many. The mariner before the mast, the lordly one who paced the quarter deck - none was so great, and none so humble, that he might not glean from him some addition to his knowledge. He gained confidence from his own commanding height and strength of arm, his straightness of back. None better then than he to guide, direct, persuade, potential trading clients - none better then than he to provide, through the Agency that employed him, efficiency of service.

Baldwins benefited. Rosina, increasingly diverted to caring for her father, took comfort knowing the Agency secure. Decline was in abeyance. Recovery was under way. And there could be no doubting the driving force behind that regeneration. George's abounding energy. It enthused others of their small community. Optimism prevailed, and even the drab little office assumed an air of gaiety, till -

His passing was peaceful. Not unexpected, it yet occasioned Rosina profound heartache. Father-daughter - the filial bond had been strong, they had worked harmoniously. Moderate success had chanced their way, and there her father would rest content. "Food in our bellies, coats on our backs, roof over our heads and *the goodwill of our neighbours* - what more?" it had pleased him to reiterate. But Rosina, for all she loved her father, *did* have need of more. Not averse to visible, tangible reward for honest labour, she had sometimes thought her parent *too* good, *too* gentle for the predatory world of commerce, whereas….

She did not fully understand this other man, the only other one to have impinged on her thirty years of life. George Munnerly disturbed. George Munnerly intrigued. George Munnerly, for good or ill, excited latent feminine desire - while possessing aspirations not far distant from her own. Beneath that youthful, Gaelic charm, she recognized a strong, determined will. Maturing, George could barely tolerate denial, would not willingly give way. But, not *offending* those of the trade, his bluff-aggressive manner stimulated growth. Here was one the City could meet on *equal* terms, one they could respect, could accept as one of their own. Munnerly/Baldwin now *delivered the goods*. Factory gate to ultimate destination – smooth passage was assured. And Rosina, free agent now and hands firmly grasping reins of office, had acquired a new and virile partner.

Tongues wagged:

"Rosina? Not old Baldwin's girl? No! Never thought I'd see the day!"

"Girl? Pushing thirty, if a day! But I wish her luck."

Rosina and George were married, without undue display, in the seamen's church of St. Nicholas, on the Liverpool waterfront, in the month of April, 1827.

"Close call, you ask me," one cynic was heard to say.

Love, could it be called, or just each seeing in the other the counterpart? Their common aim was wealth, their engine of achievement, trade. All round them was their school, the Port of Liverpool; their masters were those proficient in the greater halls of commerce. They eased their way to trading on their own account, she behind the scene and he no stranger to quayside, deck or consultation table. They profited - and Brunswick Street was first to go, for an office well appointed, staffed, equipped, in a principal street of the City. They thrived - until the name of Munnerly was flagged around the Port for shrewdness and willingness to take and benefit from calculated risk. They prospered - to build, in time, their own small fleet and partake of the booming Caribbean markets. Antigua, Havana, Kingston, Port au Prince were ever in their hearts and minds, they and the rich returns from sugar, tobacco, coffee and rum. Success, so sweet, bred more success. When Burgess, with whom they principally dealt, retired from his Jamaican plantation they hastened to declare an interest. A deal was struck, and Munnerly/Baldwin, retaining the services of competent factor, Victor Huglet, became supplier and importer of its own produce. Domestic matters only of supreme importance were suffered to impede their onward, upward progress.

On August, 3rd 1827, in a spacious, well-appointed house in Rodney Street, Liverpool, to a young father, amazement, pride and delight - to a mother of maturer years, thankfulness and joy! To Rosina and George both, a daughter – *and a son*! Rose, lovely as the flower whose name she bore, and Amos George, heir and continuator-to-be of the Munnerly line. Merchant, planter, husband, now a father; George, far-travelled from Clontarf, had much to celebrate. Yet this was not to be the end.

Clearly he saw it in his mind, the house befitting his family's elevated state, that would be the home of Munnerlys to come, and a retreat from dockside Liverpool. The land was there, *just waiting for development*. He saw it and he coveted it each day anew, across the two-mile width of the River Mersey – on the green, serene, unspoiled peninsula of Wirral. And he was not alone. Other traders, ship-owners and professionals with designs on that same land united in a corporation. *Royal Rock Ferry Company* they called themselves and he, should he desire, could make up their dozen. Just above the Wirral shore they planned an elegant, exclusive residential park. *Rock Park* it would be called. Three plots to each corporate member, one on which to build for occupation, two on which to build for purposes of sale - an opportunity never to be missed! He'd viewed preliminary plans. He'd chosen his would-be site. He'd even named his would-be home, *Havana House*. But one thing wanted. Finance at this juncture was not unlimited. Demands were in effect or pending. But still one source of revenue remained, until now resisted in practice – though invested in substantially. Most lucrative this source had proved, most profitable, and yet controversial. Here, now, should they *actively* participate, caution would be desirable.

Two hundred years and more it had enjoyed respectability. Aristocracy, men of state, ship-owners, councillors, traders, the monarchy itself: *all* had given it their blessing - while benefiting prodigiously from its rewards. Now, it was an issue of fierce debate. Trade in slaves, denounced by some, was upheld, by those who stood to lose, with specious argument. Followers of Wilberforce had won the day. Parliamentary Acts had been carried. *The Trade*, a felony now, was punishable by transportation. *The Trade* again, akin to piracy, was punishable by the hangman's noose. Yet still there were those who dared, balancing the risk of apprehension on high seas against the even greater profit. Might not he, this once, *this only once*, take one last step - and be counted among their number?

"Not while I draw breath," Rosina said. "We've travelled far enough that road, and oh yes, I know, it has paid us handsomely. But times are changing, George. Opinion is loud in its disfavour. We listen to the arguments. We follow Hansard's every word. We know the rights and wrongs,.. and we've been of a mind – till now. And the risk! – Too great for what it's worth. What's moved you, George? What is it in you that has changed?"

"Not in me," quietly, he said. "Not me, nor you, nor us – but our son, Amos George. It's Amos George makes all the difference now."

"The boy? Obsessed!" she said. "Take care, George Munnerly. Take care! This is no way for us! Nor is it that you love the boy so much – *not*, I mean, *for his own dear sake*."

"The *future*, Ros! Look beyond ourselves and even Amos George. The family, Ros, the future of the family, *our* family, *our name*! Now *that's* the thing! *The Trade?* It's here to stay, Ros, some one way or another. Ships, Navy, manufactures, commerce, not to say the luxuries - where would *any* of it be without *the Trade*? And we ourselves, Rosina Munnerly, where would *we* have been? You're party to this venture just as much as I. It's hypocrisy to reap the benefits while running down the source! *Everything's* dependent on it. Plantations, *our* plantation, without slaves? Impossible. The risk? Nothing worth the gaining comes without a little risk! This once," he'd said. "*This only once*, and then all over, finished, - and our son, *and our sons' sons*, will be the ones to thank us. And set your mind at rest, Ros, my dear," he'd said. "Nothing untoward will come upon our precious cargo. No hair of any head will suffer harm. My oath on that! It's only *I* will bear the brunt." And that was it. No more was said. But Rosina's fears were not allayed when, upon a day in the third decade of the nineteenth century, a certain three-mast ship was towed out from the River Mersey into the deep waters of Liverpool Bay.

Petrel, first of three with her sisters *Egret* and *Cormorant,* was still the nearest to her owners' hearts. Built for speed and seaworthiness she handled well, responding sweetly to the smallest trim of sail. Darling of the quarter-deck and love of the men before the mast, she was bound for West Africa, for the Gulf of Guinea, and the Slave Coast. Tow-line cast, ungainly, powerful paddle-tug visible only now by its fast-diminishing stern, she blossomed, flowered, as with a ripple of reports her pure-white sails unfurled and filled. From a thing inert she gathered way before a fair north-westerly. Not a man of that young crew was not braced for trials to come. Not a man was there who was not heart-moved by that near-organic awakening, by that transformation and departure. Not a man – save Jones.

The first mate has seen too many departures to wax sentimental over his receding homeland - and too many landfalls to wax lyrical over palm-fringed, white-sand shores. Ship for him was home, the elements his solitary world. Stout of build, muscle-hard and obdurate; he stood his watch, innately sensitive to variation of wind, deviation from course, and the *feel* of the vessel through the soles of his feet. Lone, taciturn, any lapse from proper seamanship perceived, then his tongue became a scourge, his fist a stone. Stolidly efficient now, so would he be should calamity befall. And resentful, now, that his quarter deck should be invaded by that least of all creatures, a landsman.

It sat uneasily on his conscience. *Not the way for us,* had been her words. Exercising privilege, he shared the quarter deck of his own ship, not caring to intrude upon his officers. He submitted to thoughts of a personal drift - of salient events in his life: his exit from Clontarf, the rapidity of his career, his marriage and the birth of his son, Amos George, and of his daughter. Day following day and week succeeding week, the passage was wonderfully without event - the cordage thrummed, the waters raced, and the long, white wake defined the swiftness of her flight. Crew, not over-pressed and with many a seaman's diversion to engage the languorous hours, were to a man content. But George, toward the southern latitudes, felt the weight of hours, the heat-engendered discomfort, and the tedium – were it not for evenings spent in the cabin and the company of Captain Oakshott.

He never ceased to wonder. So unlike a captain of the mercantile marine, this man whose table and finest Madeira he shared. Silver haired, ascetic, erudite, Captain Oakshott would impress as any officer of His Majesty's Navy. One such he had been. Many a sanguine account might he give of service under his heroic Nelson, but never a word would he utter on the subject of his discharge. Seaman of acknowledged competence and courage his dealing with *the Trade* was more than a passing one. "One step ahead," he was saying, gracefully at ease across the table from his guest. "So much has changed. Gone, the time we picked up cargo here and there along the Coast. Navy's changed all that. Hence the depots where the merchandise is kraaled for ease of embarkation. Speed, vigilance, decisiveness," each word he punctuated with the tap of a lean, ruby-ringed finger upon the table. "Those are the watchwords now. Vigilance on our approach, but even more upon our exit. Speedy embarkation, then clean away with not a blockading frigate in sight. Let's drink to it. Aye," he said.

Land masses, the peak of Teneriffe, Canary Islands, floated lazily, cloudily, into view on her weather side. And as imperceptibly sank below the horizon, following provisioning - until the vast continent itself gave hint of its presence, with vaporous skies on *Petrel's* leeward side. They *felt* it, they *smelled* it, the heat radiating from the vastness of its extent, the luxuriance of its vegetation. Those who had not witnessed it before thrilled to the first intimation of the huge, mysterious, life-clamorous, continent of Africa. One thousand, two thousand, three thousand more miles *Petrel* pursued her southerly course before bearing east to follow, now vaguely within sight of land, now in infinity of ocean, the Gold Coast, the Ivory Coast and last, the Coast of Slaves, there to drop anchor in the Bight of Benin.

What did George *really* know of life save that gleaned from an idyll of childhood in Ireland; from a near-monastic life in Trinity College, and from an absorbing welter of maritime activity against the backdrop of slums that shamed the Liverpool waterfront? What did he really know of *the Trade* save that let fall from the mouths of those grown rich on its profit? *Now* he could see first hand the foundations upon which those magnificent homes and that glorified gentility had been built. *Now* he could *see–*

It proceeded on an industrial scale. To the water's edge the primeval rainforest advanced. Intense, immense and ravenous, it gorged upon its own putrefaction. Oven-hot and humid, it exuded from mosquito-breeding swamps an atmosphere infused with malaria and yellow fever. *White man's grave* this coast had been called, and many times it had so proved. In sprawling barracoons, or enclosures, were herded the shackled *merchandise*. Helpless, hopeless, semi-starved and sullen, no vestige left of human dignity, they were held, the women and the men, until for some cheap factory goods they might be traded, shipped and stowed as cargo in their bodies' length and breadth, in the darkness and heat of holds below the waterline. Small wonder then many would not survive the six thousand miles of the *Middle Passage,* their carcasses dumped as wastage. But so far had George proceeded, so deeply was he embroiled, that no backward step might now be taken.

"I can advise," observed the cultivated captain whose past was veiled in secrecy, "advise," he said, "but not determine. No practical purpose would be served by your presence ashore. Aboard, you are relatively safe. There, I could not answer for. Contact, for crew and all concerned, must be minimal, cargo being brought off by canoe. Jones may be trusted for onshore proceedings, while watches aboard prepare for the new consignment. God willing, we could sail, in due time, with a full complement. But experience tells us *no*, and we should not expose ourselves without good cause. *Again* I say, *I can but advise."*

But George's mind was set. Cognizant, now, of the grim reality and despairing of his role in it, he plunged to depths of self-opprobrium. For all his meteoric rise, was he not yet young? And was it not natural that from a home where faith informed each thought, from a strict doctrinal education, was it not natural there should echo words for long disregarded. *I absolve thee from thy sin.* Oh, that *that* might be so. Could absolution be given for this and he rendered inwardly clean? But there was no priest to utter those words. Here, he must fashion his own redemption. Accepting guilt, acknowledging in the face of those he wronged his culpability - surely that would be some way, some *little* way?

First blush of dawn saw the ship's boat pull away with the distinguished passenger, the first officer and the shore-watch bathed in the sun's reflected glow. Ashore, they went their separate ways, Jones eager to engage in businesses of barter, point by point appraisal of the human *merchandise*, and the transportation of that same *merchandise* to the hold of *Petrel,* George to repair the tattered remnants of his self-esteem. But while the former fulfilled his purpose with callous efficiency, the latter's sole reward was disillusionment. Beyond reach of his compassion were the wasted bodies and spiritless eyes. Beyond all reason, was the covetous glee of the captor chiefs as they foraged obscenely among items of worthless novelty - brought by Jones and his party in payment for human life. And as the sun sank, and eerily the night calls of the forest echoed, George returned to *Petrel.*

We therefore commit his body to the deep. It was as Captain Oakshott had predicted - the Coast exacted its toll of *Petrel's* crew. Three times he intoned the words of *Burial Service at Sea.* Three times the crew stood silent, and three times the waters of Benin Bight closed over the weighted, tarpaulin-wrapped bodies of much valued mariners, two young and promising, one of tried and tested seamanship. Mercifully the endings had been swift. All aboard were relieved to exit from that pestilential coast, and hardly a one did not vow never to return. Hold filled to capacity with the objects of its sojourn, *Petrel* made for as swift a passage to the Caribbean, that wastage of cargo be minimal. *But now was the time for greatest vigilance*, the captain informed his evening guest. *Now was the time, when slavers' holds were full and prospects of head-money good, that the greater interests of Preventive Squadron crews would be served by interception and seizure.* "But odds," he went on, "are weighted in *our* favour. The *Squadron* is at best times overstretched, Naval vessels being taken out for service in more pressing spheres." It was contrary, therefore, to his spirit of optimism that, at dawn of the third day out, there floated down from the main-top crosstrees a ringing, urgent cry, "Deck, deck below there, Sai-ail!"

Pinpoint of light on the horizon, it was enough to send pulses of alarm through the veins of *Petrel's* crew. But, "Steady as she goes," coolly came the alerted Captain's order, "till identity proves positive." He had not long to wait. It was ill fortune that his ship should fall foul of a Royal Naval frigate arriving to take up station in the blockade. The vessel had *Petrel* in its sight and was in pursuit. Captain Oakshott's consultation with Chief Officer Jones and the vessel's owner, was brief. Accounting for time, for distance and the frigate's superior spread of canvas, flight would be futile. But every second gained in chase would be a second gained for disposal of the cargo, and obliterating from the hold all evidence of human habitation. And considering the penalty for apprehension in the act of slave trading, *that* could be the only recourse. Decisive the order to his Chief Officer, and loudly it was relayed to *Petrel's* boatswain and all hands, "Stand by to evacuate cargo!"

It was achieved with methodical rapidity. Hands fearing alike the consequence of seizure, the first officer's vituperative tongue and knotty fist, and the burly bosun's knout, fell to with a will. Out of the hold, out onto the sunlit deck they routed the shackled and bewildered prisoners. Stumbling, staggering, shielding their eyes, the wretched creatures poured, filling their lungs with sweet untainted air. Air and exercise - perhap? Reaching journey's end - maybe? Extreme was their terror when truth dawned. Then, by main force they were hauled, fiercely resistant or dumbly apathetic, to *Petrel's* side and pitched willy-nilly into the chill Atlantic water. Their frantic struggles were brief as weighted by their chains they sank, to begin a long, slow, silent descent to their forever-rest upon the ocean-bed. But even as they were being routed from the hold, the scouring and the ventilation were vigorously under way.

Speck of light on the dawn horizon the only constant in a shifting sea; ship hull down; ship in detail down to gun-ports and ensign; ship with a bone of whiteness in is teeth and gaining visibly – such were the observations of Captain Oakshott throughout the course of that long day. Each glimpse gave spur to the cleansing. Then a puff of smoke from one of the frigate's guns, distant report - and a spout of water not a cable's length forward of *Petrel's* bow. Sail shortened, way lost, hove-to, she waited. All that could be done, the Captain was grimly satisfied, had, indeed, been done.

His thoroughness won the day. Much to the chagrin of the boarding officer's party and the frigate's crew, search as they might, no vestige of occupation of the hold for unlawful purpose could be found. Thwarted of salvage and head-money they still might strongly suspect; but suspicion alone would not hold in an Admiralty Court. And, *Petrel* allowed to proceed on her course, suspense was lifted from Captain Oakshott and his crew. But, now heading for the Caribbean Sea and the Munnerly estate, a weight as of chains hung in the region of George Munnerly's heart.

The three occupants of a house in Liverpool's broad and gracious Rodney Street were waiting. *Petrel* in the offing after more than three long years, the news had straightway been relayed to Rosina. "Papa coming home!" Many times the twins had listened to their mother's words. Many times had little Amos and little Rose returned her gaze with wide-eyed infant curiosity. *Papa?* - Who *was* this strange *Papa* Mama was talking of? Dimly, distantly, his shadowy figure loomed. Soon they would *know*. Soon would sound of hoof and wheel be heard and a carriage seen beyond the drawing-room window. Who would be first to hear, and who to see? Rose was quick to seize the window seat, while Amos, indecisive, hovered. And then, would he alight to take the steps in two large bounds? Would he gather up the children, one in each great arm? Would laughter affront the dignity of that superior drawing-room as, nearly to the ceiling, he tossed the pair?

The touch of his lips was upon her cheek. And courtesy

was there in his embrace. But passion? That had featured only briefly in their marriage pact, before partnership, social, domestic and business, had taken precedence. Shyly, the children sought refuge in the folds of their mother's skirts. And she, late comer to the married state and still proud in the magnitude of his presence, his moulded masculinity of feature, sensed constraint in this reunion. Some insubstantial barrier interposed, in his eyes, a haunted, hunted, look. But there was no time for questioning. Matters must come to light in a manner of their own choosing. Meanwhile, he had a not unpleasant duty to perform …

"Little things," he said, "picked up along the way for you. A moment." His absence was brief, and returning he bore a small sea-going chest, brassbound, handsome, personal. In lesser hands than his it would have been considerable weight. He set it down, and the children, curiosity-emboldened, gathered, kneeling, to watch the movements of his hands. He produced a key - and with affected ceremony inserted it. The click was barely audible. He swung open the convex lid.

"Who first?" he said.

"Mama, of course." And her answer winning his approval, he reached into the chest to produce a parcel neatly wrapped, and handed it to Rose. "For you," he said. "For *you* to give to your Mama." And holding it with care Rose passed the parcel to her mother. The shawl, of rich, harmonious colouring, was of a texture soft and warm. She draped it round her shoulders and thanked him with her eyes, her smile. For her, also, there was a slide of tortoise shell inset with semi-precious stones, that nestled in her dark hair. For Rose there was an inlaid box, that opening gave out a tinkling melody and set in motion a graceful, dancing figure. For her also a brooch of fine silver, setting a milky, red-veined, green-veined, opalescent stone. "Not for now," he said, "but for when you are a lady. Take good care of it." But the gift for Amos – that must be handled with especial care….

No toy, this craft was a product of skill, of infinite patience, and of time. *Petrel!* Perfect in its every detail it was, in its entirety, a work of seaman's art. The mariner-maker had observed keenly during long sea hours and with his sailor's ingenuity had fashioned it. Now George watched, to study its effect upon his little son.

The boy was nothing if not deep. No exclamation of delight, no change in the stillness of his features, only in the intensity of his gaze, his complete absorption and single-minded concentration. With knitted brow and slender fingers he traced the contours of this wonderful thing, its intricacies of superstructure, sails and cordage. George nodded, satisfied - no time too soon, no occasion too small or big, to acquaint the boy with his intended destiny!

"Yes," said George, when at last they were alone. The plantation was in good shape. The factor, Victor Huglet, was all that Burgess had led him to believe. Revenue from cane and coffee was good. If such continued, the purchase-debt would soon be repaid. The man was good, too, with the slaves in his charge. Firm but fair, he liked to think, where brutality often was the norm. Unfortunate necessity! *Havana House* would take its course, would have to wait. But it was well they had secured the site. Not a word had George to say upon a subject closer to Rosina's heart, when she and he had differed acrimoniously. But she would not press that issue. Not yet awhile...

"Amos," instead, her protest was mild, "is young for such a gift. He is a child, George, a *little* child."

"Amos is the future, and not just yours and mine. When I am gone, *and* you too, Ros, the name, the family, of Munnerly, I am determined, must not perish with us. All *we*'ve achieved, or *will* achieve - what in heaven is it for, if not only a beginning? And did you not see the way he took it in? So serious! That boy's to be his *father's* son, my dear. Now let's be clear. Let us *both* be clear on that!"

"I understand," Rosina said. "You may be right. But, *that boy,* as you put it, is my son too. I *am* his mother, George. It is *I* have borne and raised him, and seen him in a *mother's* light. Amos George has eyes for everything. He thinks. He's inward looking. And are you not forgetting that we have a daughter, too?"

"Do you look after *Rose, my dear* - and leave the boy to me."

Time's passing: Rosina could not but remark the changes. A smooth-skinned youth her husband had departed - a man he had returned. He was even taller-seeming now, being sparer and more angular - taller, with a darker set of countenance. Time alone could not have etched those lines upon his cheek. Experience had put *them* there. Her ebullient, her inspired and inspiring George, her partner, was grimly-driven now. Work, *Havana House,* the boy were all obsessions. And diversions? That newfound taste for drink, that uncertainty of mood; these gave further cause for her concern.

Work, Havana House and Amos George - if not one, then another claimed ascendancy. Liverpool, whose vitality had once won the heart of an Irish lad, was vital still – and more. The seaport city, second to none in the world, was in the midst of unrelenting growth. The driving force was steam - steam-powered transport land and sea. Speedy, efficient, reliable and voluminous, it stimulated trade - in cotton and in manufactured goods. It stimulated the building of flour mills, of sugar refining factories, and more and yet more docking space. And those wretched dwellings of the abject poor, so long a scar on the city's face; even they must go, and be replaced. And Munnerly and Company must have a hand in everything, be in the van of change – or by their standards fail. George, of Munnerly and Company, had much to keep his body and his mind in occupation. And when exhaustion threatened, as from time to time it did, he looked across the two-mile width of the Mersey, as to a haven of respite and repose.

Two Mersey miles, so near - and yet so far in otherworldly peace - the green of Wirral beckoned. When in 1817 a steam ferry first linked Liverpool with the Birkenhead suburb of Rock Ferry, it opened the way for the concept of residential Rock Park to become reality. Plans had been drawn, but not until 1837 was the detailed draft approved. Three dozen palatial mansions, individually designed, each in its substantial garden, would be threaded through by an elegant circular driveway. It was a citadel of peace for those who could afford it. Undesirables would be deterred by payment of toll. Here would be *Havana House.* Backing upon the Mersey shore it would command a view of the river traffic and the Liverpool waterfront. And there, upon his chosen site, might be seen the tall figure of George Munnerly musing upon the time of its completion. He would not always be alone.

A singular pair they made, not unfamiliar about the waterfront, the docks and offices - George Munnerly, and son. Bearing the small child on his shoulder, leading the boy by the hand, striding step for step with the growing lad, George Munnerly let no chance pass that would ease the boy into his intended role in life: worthy successor to the Munnerly estate, custodian of all its concerns, and progenitor of the Munnerly dynasty.

"Must I, Mama?" The heir-apparent of the Munnerly fortunes was urgent in his appeal. "Must I, *must* I go? Can he not *see*, Mama? Can he not *understand*? May I not say to him, Mama, *I'd rather not this once.* It's *here* I belong, doing those things I *want* to do. May I not stay with you and Rose? And his people, Mama, are not my people. They talk, Mama, they talk so loud. They talk, but not to me, Mama, except they fuss and then forget that I am there. And I am tired, Mama, I am not well, and sometimes think, Mama, that I could die. And I have not yet finished my picture."

"Tell him, Mama," his sister said. "Tell Amos that he *has* to go. He knows what happened last time. I cannot bear *his* silences, *his* storms. And now I lie awake at night, Mama, waiting, and then I listen for the turning of his key, and I hear the beating of my heart. I count each step along the passageway, and then, Mama, I listen for the voices. I hate the way he shouts. We love you, Amos - but tell him, Mama. For all our sakes – tell Amos that he *has to go*."

One more, he told himself. *One more before time's called and I must quit the warmth and comfort of The Tusk. One last, to slip, tonight, into blessed oblivion of sleep.*

"Usual Mr. Munnerly?" the landlord said.

"Madeira," he said. "And this time not so sparing with the measure."

....always the same, the dream. Tall as I, the man, who with his bearing might have been a chief. He looks me squarely in the eye and I see there nothing but contempt. He thrusts his chained wrists before my face as if to say, 'These are nothing to the ones that you will bear for the rest of your life.' And he walks away- but the screams! Then nothing, nothing but the silence and the stillness of the water. She knows! I know she knows...

They are against me, all the three. They will not look me in the face, as if they have something to fear... the gift that I had thought so wonderful, so right for him, I thought, shattered into a thousand pieces.

"Time Mr. Munnerly," the landlord said.

The brass-bound box hadn't come with a key. Judging by the rust it hadn't been touched in living memory. I was trying to prize it open with a screwdriver when the stupid thing slipped and cut my hand. Now I was dripping blood onto the tiles and rummaging in the drawer with my good hand.

'What's up?' Phil's expression showed a mixture

of concern and exasperation. He must've long ago overcome his surprise that someone who'd once made their living as a dancer could be so uncoordinated.

'Cut myself.'

He dabbed the cut with TCP and I struggled not to jump. 'What were you trying to do?'

'Open this damned thing.' The small padlock securing the hasp was scratched but still intact.

Phil shook his head. 'A screwdriver's no use. Where did it come from anyway?'

'Great Aunt Flo's stuff. '

'Dunno why you bother.' He shrugged. 'Bolt cutter'll do it.'

'Because I want to know what really happened to Rose, who just disappears, apparently. And to poor Amos- on that last day.'

Havana House, Rock Park pictured around 1900. It can be seen that the original garden trees have matured.

CHAPTER 3

Liverpool's Black Community

The Liverpool Black community is arguably the oldest in Britain but although slaves were sold at places like the Exchange Coffee House from the eighteenth century the origins of the community are more varied and surprising.

Britain encouraged African chiefs to send their children to England for an education in order to consolidate the 'friendship' with these rulers. Numbers could be substantial with between 50 and 80 African boys attending the Bluecoat School each year and in the 1780's girls as well as boys were being sent to Liverpool. And boarding with local families. This continued well beyond the days of the Slave Trade. Other European powers had the same idea and the more politically astute chieftains placed their children in several countries to secure maximum advantage.

It was not without its risks. Sometimes the children never reached Britain. Newspapers in Nassau record on February 22nd 1799 that two young African boys, the sons of King John Qua Ben, a major chief in Gabon, had been sold in Havana. It was not an isolated case.

Other black settlers arrived after the American War of Independence (1775-1783). The British, outnumbered and unable to rely on reinforcements arriving, decided to recruit slaves. Lord Dunmore, the British Royal Governor of Virginia offered freedom to all who deserted their American rebel masters. Black regiments were formed with white officers, initially in non combatant roles but by the end of the war black troops were fighting on both sides.

After the British surrendered at York Town black loyalists sought a new life in British-owned possessions and when the British left Charleston they took with them 5000 black soldiers. Thousands more accompanied the regular troops from Savannah and New York.

For those who chose to come to Britain times were hard. Often unable to find work many were destitute, especially in London. It was decided to offer resettlement in Sierra Leone and although there was some reluctance, in April 1787 some 350 colonists departed including 41 black women and 50 white wives showing that inter-racial marriage was not uncommon. Although rare, it was not unknown for girls of good family to marry black men of 'good family'.

Some however remained in Liverpool and the parish registers of St James show a number of people giving their birthplace as America.

Black sailors form one of the largest contributions, both slaves and free. The Elder Dempster line had a particular tradition of employing black sailors and maintained a hostel for them. Initially they had equal pay but after the seamen's strike in 1911 whites were paid twice as much which created increased racial disharmony where for many years there had been a degree of mutual acceptance.

Hardly surprising, then, to find that attitudes reflected the spirit of the times in the Munnerly family...

Amos

The grandfather clock - a fine example by Finney of Liverpool - struck eleven as Amos drained his glass. Then Havana House was quiet again. If he didn't retire soon, old George Munnerly, the resident ogre, would be down. It shamed him to think that at fifty-three he was still afraid of his father, but it was the truth.

He knew the exact day in May 1840 when fear had first taken possession of him. They were still living in the town house in Rodney Street. Thin walled with its rooms stacked one upon another, privacy was scarce. Unable to contain his curiosity when he heard his father's raised voice he stopped to listen and caught Rosina's reply, not loud but icy. *'I'm your wife George. You can't throw* ***me*** *overboard.'*

All the old whispered stories flooded his imagination- about slaves being jettisoned to lighten the ship in a storm and evade capture by the naval patrols, or simply because the price had dropped and insurance become a more profitable alternative. The loss could be entered as 'brown sugar' on the manifest. Shaken, he crept upstairs. There were black boys at the Bluecoat which he attended, sons of chiefs sent over for an English education. One – Joseph - he knew well enough for friendship. Unbearable to think of that sharp mind and impish spirit being drowned beneath the murky waters of the Atlantic.

'Amos? Is that you?'

Rose, his sister. He need not let her know.

‘What d’you want?’ Not his usual tone: he must be careful. Rose was quick to sense when anything was wrong. Maybe it was because they were twins although there was little physical resemblance between them.

‘Are you quite well?’ Her face in memory was still babyishly round and dusted with pale freckles, brows drawn together in puzzlement.

‘Yes’.

‘You sounded .....odd.‘

‘No, um....no-’

But to the mature man safe in his own room these images returned unbidden and often. The frantic struggle as you were dragged to the rail. The dreadful fall. The desperate gasp before the water closed over you. Light becoming dim, warmth dying away, lungs bursting with the need for air. Caught between the urge to breathe and the knowledge that this breath would be your last.... Amos realised that he was crying and scrubbed away the tears on his sleeve. It was a lifetime ago but the knowledge, and the attempt to conceal it had burdened him all his subsequent days. He looked around the dim, over-furnished library in something like bewilderment. Firelight flickered on hand-blocked wallpaper, patterned with green fleur de lys, on paintings of ships in ornate, gilded frames and the towering mahogany bookshelves filled with the serried ranks of unread volumes, each bound in matching morocco. He smiled wryly. Another of his father’s bargains, bought by the yard at the bankruptcy sale of some great house after the stock market crash of ’66. Thick Persian rugs, layered over the Turkey carpet, and heavy velvet curtains, released from their complex cords for the night, shut out draughts but deadened all sound of the world outside. A private kingdom but not his

Again voices from the past: 1854 and he was one year married.

‘Rock Park, that’s the place.’

‘Surely it would be more convenient to stay in the city

father?' He'd hoped to move out but without George's agreement it would not be affordable.

'Don't want my grandsons dying of cholera.' George glanced over at Joan who blushed, uncomfortable at having attention drawn to her condition. 'Waste of money that damned Duncan fella turned out to be. Medical Officer of Health indeed!'

'Living conditions are bad- so many people out of work.' Amos felt he had to try to set the record straight.

The older man nodded coolly. 'Rock Park it is. Already bought a plot.'

That familiar burning ache assaulted Amos' stomach. He poured another measure of brandy anyway. Deadening of his spiritual pain must take precedence over the damage he might be doing to his body. His hand was unsteady and the golden liquid slopped out over the fringed chenille cloth. But he no longer cared. Replacing the decanter he became aware of the glassy eyes of stuffed birds under their domes. Barn and tawny owls, kestrel and some fanciful arrangements of smaller birds in a 'natural' setting. He never much cared for them but tonight their un-winking gaze was chilling: a silent jury weighing the evidence against him. There was a huge weight of it, pressing down on him tonight, on mind and heart. He could stand it no longer and made his retreat taking the decanter with him.

Across the wide hall, he lurched, shadowy now with most of the gaslights extinguished, and up the stairs to the gallery. He glanced back to where the family portrait, crowded with his progeny, hung in pride of place. He sniggered to himself. George hadn't done too well with that purchase. The boy might claim to be an artist but his draughtsmanship left much to be desired. The way Alice's head sat on her neck might have been inspired by a visit to the gallows and what a mistake to give the girls bare feet even if they were appropriate with the classical drapes! Pig's trotters had more grace.

But the merriment was short-lived. The picture was another

testament to his failure. How pale and drained his wife looked and small wonder. Fourteen pregnancies and nine children still living. George's demand for a male heir had ruined a marriage which had started with every promise of happiness. Five daughters in six years had seen to that. After the last, a particularly difficult delivery, he'd been only too aware of the way Joan shrank from him when he climbed into their bed. Alcohol had helped to dull his sensibilities to the blue eyes strained and afraid when he looked down. 'Maybe it'll be a boy this time.'

It hadn't been.

'Another girl!' George's face blazed frustration, the mouth thinned to a hard line. Amos decided to invoke the Almighty as one opponent his father couldn't browbeat.

'We have to accept what God sends father.'

But George's belligerence only increased. 'Pah! Mealy mouthed nonsense.' Then, in malice 'Perhaps you should see a doctor?'

Amos flushed remembering his embarrassment. 'That's not necessary.'

'Give me my grandson!'

Now Joan was exhausted, old before her time – and less vital than Rosina who was fast approaching eighty but retaining all the familiar energy and will.

The bedroom from which she'd finally fled, with its heavy, carved wardrobe and four poster became a place of solitary regrets. But tonight it seemed filled with ghosts. Some perverse instinct made him take out the locked box from its hiding place under the bed and spread the contents on the counterpane. His degree. Christening cards for his many children. Packets containing locks of hair and baby teeth. A scrapbook. Cufflinks bought for his twenty-first birthday. A collection of ancient sketch books. Almost at random he began to leaf through one.

He'd been in his teens when he'd painted these. Interiors of the town house with its steep stairs and paneled walls and the imported Austrian crystal chandelier that had been Rosina's pride and joy. It now hung in the morning room because she couldn't bear to leave it behind. Even at the distance of forty years he thought the pictures had rough merit.

'*You want to do what?*'

'Study art father.'

'You're going into the business'

'Everyone says I have talent .....'

George's face had warned him that he'd already gone too far. 'No son of mine will be dependent on patronage.'

There had been no question of contesting the point although he'd continued to paint in his leisure time. He flipped open another book. Water-colours of the city, fine buildings and tiny figures busy about their daily activities. Then, near the back, some informal portraits, all of females. Rosina in her favourite burgundy taffeta, sitting in the barred sunlight from the long morning room window. Two of the maids preparing vegetables in the scullery.....and Rose.

August 1842. A fifteen year old girl in a blue dress and is holding a spaniel puppy. Bella. He had to think for a moment before he could bring the animal's name to mind. Increasingly his memory was unreliable. So far he'd been able to cover these shortcomings but how much longer could that last?

He ran thickened fingers gently over the painted page. The only image of Rose which remained: it was a good likeness. Delicate features...creamy skin and a figure that was already alluring. There had been plenty of suitable young men interested in Rose. Why in God's name couldn't she have chosen one of them? He rubbed his eyes. What a disaster it had been. If he'd had access to her journal, left behind in the rapidity of her escape, he would have realized sooner which way her thoughts were running:

I met Joseph again at the Williamsons' Christmas party. I feared he had been invited as much for his curiosity value as his father's vast wealth and that he must be aware of it, but he seemed perfectly at ease and looked wonderfully exotic in a crimson coat and sand coloured trousers. He complemented me on my dress and remarked how well my name suited me saying that to him I seemed the perfect English rose. I forbore to mention that in fact very little of my ancestry is English.

For the first time I saw him as I might have seen any young man of my own class. He is tall and well formed with a peculiarly graceful carriage. Although his skin is dark there are reddish tones like the rich warmth of mahogany and his eyes are surprisingly light and set at an angle. His features are finer than one would expect. The nose short and straight, the mouth most beautifully shaped and the teeth dazzling. There is something of the look of Egypt about him and I begin to understand the allure of that ancient land.

Maybe it had always been too late. He could recall a visit to the circus as children and how Rose had been entranced by the power and beauty of the beasts. Perhaps her love affair with Africa had started then. In any case, that sweet face belied a will as implacable as her father's. George had always spoiled her of course. 'The spit of my mother' he would say, and his hard, dark eyes would brighten with sentimental tears. Rose had only to ask to be given anything she wanted. It had not been the same for him. George had always expected more than Amos had to give. He took another swallow of brandy.

August 1848 and Rose and he had just celebrated their twenty first birthday with a huge party, attended by more notables and business associates of their father than their own friends. Rose was making a list of the gifts, preparatory to writing dozens of dutiful 'thank you' letters, seated at the monstrous table that still adorned the house. It was a task he was happy to leave to her if she would allow it. She was holding a gold and garnet necklace up to the light, admiring its rich colours when, almost casually, she made her announcement.

'We're getting married.'

The idea was preposterous. ‘You can’t marry Joseph!’

‘Why not? He’s handsome, charming, educated. When his father dies he’ll be rich.’

‘For God’s sake Rose!’

Her voice became wheedling. ‘We wanted you to be a witness.’

‘I can’t let you do it.’

‘You can’t stop me.‘ Her chin went up. ‘The arrangements are made.’

Despite differences in gender, age, colouring and features, the expression was George’s.

‘I’ll tell father,’ he threatened.

Rose shook the ringlets from which the tortoiseshell comb was always promising to slip. ‘Unless you promise to keep our secret I’m going to Joseph’s lodgings right now and then they’ll have to let me marry him.’ Rose linked her arm through his and looked up at him with those luminous eyes. ‘I love him, Amos.’

‘Father will kill me.’

Her long, fine hand had stroked his cheek. ‘Poor Amos. I know I’m not being fair to you but you shouldn’t worry. Papa will forgive you. He wants me to be happy.’

Now he shook his head, ‘Not this time Rose. He’ll never forgive either of us.’

George, in his forties, had been in his prime and formidably strong. *‘Where is she?’*

‘I don’t know.’ One thing he did know was that if he told George of Rose’s whereabouts, the scandal of her marriage would be submerged in the greater scandal of an abrupt widowhood.

‘It’s your fault. She‘d never have met him but for you.’

Amos had paid for that perceived betrayal. Never given the responsibility that he craved or that everyone agreed was his due. Even now George delayed handing over control of the Munnerly line. So why, Amos asked himself, had he never deserted the hated prison of Havana House? There was only one answer to that. He was weak.

He turned to the yellowed paper and Rose's bold hand, dated November 1851.

It seems so long since I left yet it is scarcely two years. We have a son now and named him for you. Joseph is devoted as ever. His father wishes him to take subordinate wives as is the custom but he is adamant that he will not. You would be surprised at the degree of comfort here. Indeed I have so many servants that Queen Victoria is less well attended.

It is all very different but wonderfully beautiful. Monkeys chatter in the branches and white egrets paddle in the shallows. It is never cold and fruits and blossoms hang on the trees all year round. An earthly paradise but not without its serpents. I have seen no lion but there are elephants and leopards and in the river, crocodile and hippopotamus. I do not fear for myself for Joseph has taught me to shoot and you would be amazed at my proficiency, but I worry for the children.

I miss you so much. Could you not visit? There is much that I would like to say that cannot go into a letter. Father still has interests here so a ship would not be difficult. Has he forgiven me? Perhaps some day we might even come home?

Of all his failures that, perhaps was the worst. He had never made the journey. Nor had he replied and no more letters ever followed. Had she died or did Rose also learn to regard him as a lost cause?

When he attempted to refill his glass, he found the decanter empty. Sitting at his dressing table he began to write.

'Find anything interesting?' Phil asked me later.

I just nodded.

The mystery of what had happened to Rose was solved. What courage the girl had had, and how little common sense. How long had she survived in such an alien climate? It was something to bear in mind for the future.

Amos deserved my sympathy. For a sensitive soul, having George as a father must have been a nightmare. No wonder he needed drink. There had always been a bit of a mystery about the circumstances of his death. A fall, it was said, from the gallery straight to the unforgiving marble below. I no longer doubted that it was suicide. *Rosina had known it.* Unable to tear up the unfinished note, the last thing she had of him, she'd hidden it away. Should I include it, even now? Expose him, long after all those concerned were dead? Would I be betraying Amos, who had experienced enough misery in his lifetime?

In the meanwhile there were plenty of other Munnerlys to consider - starting with his son, Henry. Family tradition had him down as something of a hero.

Statue of cherub playing a pipe, one of a pair of stone figures commissioned by Amos (presumably on his father's instructions) for the rear terrace of Havana House. They were from renowned stone carvers Farmer and Brindley of Bradford and commissioned at the time of the house's remodeling in 1872. The second figure is described as ' beating a small drum'.

Both were thought either lost or destroyed during the 1960's, however this singleton has recently turned up in a garden in Liverpool.

CHAPTER 4

Everything relating to Henry's affairs was contained in a large brown envelope tied with pink, legal ribbon. The wax seal was broken. Someone had looked at the contents before, but who? The best candidate was his eldest son, Arthur. It was likely that these papers had come back to the Munnerlys when the family solicitor died in the 1919 influenza epidemic since by then Arthur would have been married to said solicitor's daughter. I lifted the package. There was a hard bulge in the centre. Not just documents then. I tipped out the contents onto the table top.

There wasn't a great deal. A gold watch, a signet ring with the initials H and C linked together, several newspaper clippings, now brittle and yellowing and a couple of bundles of papers. I spread them out and uncovered a small, oilskin package with two locks of hair, one straight and blonde, the other one wavy and deepest brown. The blond one probably belonged to his wife but the other was a mystery. I laid it to one side and sifted through the papers.

They were mostly routine but an exchange of correspondence between the solicitor and Henry's widow caught my attention.

Caroline was clearly piqued by the solicitor's refusal to divulge information...

Linklater & Stewart,
Solicitors,
32, Dale Street,
Liverpool.
28th March,1902

Dear Mrs. Munnerly,

I am in receipt of your letter of 25th March for which I thank you.

With regard to your husband's Will, I am unable to furnish you with any details or personal reasons which may lie behind the legacy made to a Pearl Mazorro of Havana, Cuba. May I suggest that, owing to Mr. Henry Munnerly's many associations over time, it may well be a long standing debt from an earlier business transaction, which is thus repaid? I hope this explanation will suffice and I would advise that you accept it and put your mind at rest.

With kind regards, I remain

Yours sincerely,

Edmund Linklater

Edmund Linklater,
Senior Partner.

Henry

He stood six feet tall, lean and lithe, his cotton shirt, wet with tropical sweat, clinging to his shoulders. His hair, the colour of burnt rope, was tied at the nape of his neck, his gold braided cap pulled down to shade him from the sun's fierce rays. He barked his orders, "Half ahead, slow ahead, dead slow. Stop." The *Cressida* bumped gently against the dock in Port Havana. His heart raced. The smell of the Caribbean thrilled him; the bitter sweet scent of molasses, smoke and baked sweat. A place where hard men lived hard lives and women waited.

Captain Henry Munnerly had had a good voyage. The winds were fair from the Azores, where they called to replenish supplies. Well pleased with how the engines had performed, he understood why steam was taking over from sail. To think, no more wasted time lying becalmed. 1902- a new century, full steam ahead, he smiled at his own wit and shouted to the first mate standing on the foc'sle head. "Mr Morris, that the *Casablanca* ahead?"

"Aye, aye, Sir, it is. Captain Eli Jacob's ship out of Lagos."

Henry Munnerly knew whose ship it was alright and fell silent. The sight of tattered grey canvas sails flapping around naked masts disgusted him: the decks littered with tackle, slack ropes and empty livestock crates was revealing. Sailors leaned lazily against the bulwark, their spittle frothing on the surface of the sea. The Plimsoll line was barely visible for the salt encrusted barnacles covered in weed; useful in an over loaded ship, Henry thought. Rumour had it that Jacob acquired the ship from an Irishman in a hurry to get rid of it. Of Eli Jacob there was no sign.

Down in his cabin he poured himself a large rum and began to make plans. It was years since they'd last met but Henry's anger rose as he thought how sweet vengeance would be. His beloved Pearl would have to wait. Eli Jacob would not forget this night - if he could ever remember anything at all afterwards. Much older than Henry, Jacob was powerfully built and swarthy. It was said his mix of blood made him a formidable enemy. Did the scar on Jacob's cheek still flash pink on the bronzed skin? That token from a pistol whipping, the last time they'd met.

The first mate tapped on the cabin door. "Come in Morris and sit down. Rum? I want a lookout posted on the wharf, day and night. Every item of cargo that comes out of the *Casablanca,* log it and count the 'African crew'. Bastard won't get away with it much longer." As a Munnerly, Henry knew people in the Customs and at the Admiralty.

"Aye, aye, Sir." Morris cupped his hands around his mug and studied closely the Master's face. He knew there was bad feeling between the two men, but not how it started.

Darkness fell quickly and the moon hung low in a navy blue sky. Descending the gangway Henry pulled his coat about him. The nights could turn cold out here and this would be a long one. He knew where he'd look for old Eli Jacob - any bar, any brothel, any gambling den. The man's reputation was well known in ports across the new world and the old. A practised gambler who rarely lost, and one, who, when he did, exacted his revenge remorselessly upon the winner. He wondered if the man's gross appetites had changed in years. Tales of his brutality abounded. His liking for young African girls was notorious. Led to his cabin in the black of night their terrified screams could sometimes be heard in the decks below, where their mothers wept. Henry had good reason to believe the stories he had heard.

In the first bar, downing a stiff Jamaica rum, he didn't see Ramos until the young Puerto Rican until he was at his elbow.

"Packet for you Cap'n Sir. Special bacca, big packet for ya."

Henry, taking the brown paper packet, slipped coins into Ramos's filthy hands.

He went out to cool his head, making his way down narrow alleys where street urchins waited for any drunken sailor whose pocket they could pick. Their clothes hung about their skeletal bodies like rags on a chair, their faces streaked sticky brown with molasses they'd scavenged from casks in the dockside sheds. Keeping their distance they followed until he turned a corner and disappeared down steps. His boots made little noise on the flagstone floor of the tavern filled with groups of men at round wooden tables, grey with grime. Each had bare arms scarred deeply cutting sugar canes. Light from hurricane lamps dancing and flickering picked out men at their tables, drawing and puffing pipes and cigarillos. The atmosphere was pure smoke and sweat. Above the din of their voices could be heard the click of mah-jong tiles from a table of Chinese coolies. At one corner sat the women, their cheap beads glittering in the flickering light and rolling about their ample bosoms, while furtively watching for male leers. Wedged at one side was a large vat of rum watched over by two odious custodians. At one table bigger than the rest sat Eli Jacob, his stomach pressed against the edge, his sleeves rolled up the fat arms. His hair hung long and lank. About his neck and loosely knotted was a red neckerchief. A brooding gaze fell on everything. When Henry caught his attention other men at the table slunk away. No-one noticed the little Puerto Rican creep in and position himself to see what he hoped would be the mother of all fights.

The room grew quiet; stealthy figures edged back clearing a pathway for Henry.

Eli Jacob lent back in his chair, cheeks florid and his flabby jowls wobbling. "Hey! You'll not find your woman at home Munnerly. Down at the docks with the Yankee sailors," he sneered.

Henry, jaw set, eyes blazing, dragged Eli Jacob to his feet with a string of oaths. "Jacob, you're a liar, a stinking foul-mouthed liar." A fist pounded into the soft belly and moved upward to the bloated face.

Pearl, he must find her.

Once outside, the cold night air clarified his thoughts. Now he needed her more than ever, longed to hold her, lie with her as he yearned each night. Such are the dreams of sailors when staring at the seductive sea. His feet trod the well known path to their little house. If Eli Jacob were dead….? Well… he'd wanted to kill him ever since he first set eyes on him…

It had happened on that night of the year when the plantation labourers, most of them former slaves, were allowed out to sing and dance in the streets of Havana. They wore costumes, a riot of colour. Drums beat out intoxicating rhythms all night long. As they sang their haunting songs and waved their arms and stamped their feet, their garments swung in time to the music. As birds on the wing they flung their arms skyward, feeling freedom. Dark skins glistened with the sweat of vibrant young bodies rebelling against captivity and revelling without pause. A scent did the dancing forms give off so powerful it filled the air, willing their masters to smell the desire and heed their cries.

Henry was on his way back to his ship when he heard the frantic screams. *Socorro, ayudame, violacion.* He understood those words. In a dark doorway he could smell the girl's frenzied fear, the stench of stale sweat and the rum. He could hardly make out the tangle of bodies as he pulled the man away. With more strength than he knew he had he punched the attacker to the ground and in the moonlight kicked him over, stared into the bloody face of Eli Jacob.

The girl crawled away on all fours. Sobbing hysterically she got up clutching her bloodstained clothes to her thighs and began running wildly. Lost, violated and vomiting with revulsion. *Que horror, mi honor.*

"I'll not hurt you, let me help you!" Henry called as he moved slowly towards her. As he got closer, his arms outstretched, in the manner of cornering a wild filly, he could see her golden skin and dark eyes, a child, no more than twelve or thirteen years old. "I'll not hurt you, don't be frightened." She ran from him and crouched in a doorway now a cornered wild-cat. "Is this where you live?" Henry took his eyes off her momentarily to find out their whereabouts. By the look of the houses made of mud brick and crudely plastered, he knew it was in the outskirts of the town where the indigenous peoples lived. A low rumble of thunder rolled overhead and large splashes of heavy tropical ran fell noisily on the tin roofs. Wind rustled the leaves of mango trees and as the boughs dipped and swayed fruit bounced onto the ground. Moving forward to shelter under the lean-to he stepped on a mango that squelched and crushed, re-coiling at the illusion of stamping on flesh. When Henry made to knock on the door she spoke, her voice husky with fear. "No, no. Ingenio Plantation, Master Marshall."

Henry knew Jack Marshall. He'd carried cargo for him, off loaded in Liverpool and then to lucrative markets further afield. Marshall came to the island from his native Yorkshire as a surveyor. Not a man to miss an opportunity, it was known that his land was some of the most fertile around and he quickly established a place for himself in the Colonial hierarchy as a man with useful friends. He prospered from the burgeoning trade in tobacco, sugar and rum. The climate suited him as did the young women. He made his own rules, maintaining strict authority over the workers, yet they respected him. Even after abolition, most stayed on in his frugal employ. Though conditions had improved, subservience would take generations to change. Henry thought he'd treat the girl decently so long as no cost was involved. "Come with me, you'll be alright." She looked at him, distrust in her eyes and continued in a huddled heap. He moved towards her and gently lifted her stiff body, her hands still clutching her bloodstained clothes. In the silence he could feel her rapid heartbeat and her cold young body relax in his own warmth. He spoke softly as he trudged along the sandy road to the plantation. Her long dark hair had tangled with red and gold ribbons that were strewn over her shoulders. Her face was stained with tears. A wave of tenderness engulfed him as he felt her budding breasts firm against him. His arms ached as he trudged along the dusty track, his boots slipping on the pebbly gravel. Yet he found the strength and balance to keep going; too fearful to put her down lest she run away. At the side of the track he came to the stump of a cedar tree and needing a rest he sat down. As he lifted the girl onto his shoulder, her body jerked in a spasm of fear and her eyes, the colour of pewter, snapped open. Cradling her head close to him he could feel her hot breath on his neck. Sighing deeply he stroked her hair until she quietened. The tang of bushland after rain, the acrid smell of hot pepper trees and the fresh scent of cypress palms was overwhelming. In the mist of the early morning, before the sun lipped over the hill tops the troggan bird flew like a bullet to its nest in the tree trunk. The flash of blue, red and white feathers startled Henry. With his strength restored he carried on. Cane crops on either side towered over him, bowing and sighing in the night breeze but at last he could see the shape of the buildings at the Ingenio and quickened his steps. A large house in the centre was where he made for. And stepped onto the veranda. He lowered the girl down onto a cane chair and thumped hard on the heavy door.

It opened and an old African stood holding a hurricane lantern up to Henry's face. "Call your master, tell him Captain Munnerly."

The man began to protest. "Too early to wake master."

"Do as I damn well say." One proper look at Henry's countenance and he disappeared.

Silence was broken by a "What time is this? What do

you want at this hour? *I'm coming!*" Jack Marshall strode down the passage, tugging the coat about him, with his night shirt flapping around his ankles. Both men knew there was more at stake than a broken night's sleep.

"The girl here has been raped, savaged more like. Ever I see the bastard who did this I'll kill him. I swear to God I will. Get her to a doctor, Jack; I'll pay whatever it takes."

Jack Marshall was silent and surprised to see Henry so angry. He'd only seen him calm and in control. "Come inside Henry. Coffee, tot of rum?" The African servant had sloped off into the kitchen and soon appeared with a bottle of rum, which he put on the long mahogany table.

"Sit down, sit down Henry." Jack Marshall poured them both some steaming coffee and a large measure of rum. Henry slumped into the leather armchair and put his head in his hands. The sound of footsteps on the floorboards alerted him. The woman, clad only in an ivory silk gown entered the room. Both men fell silent. She looked at Henry with dark eyes and held his gaze for a long time and then came close as she reached over to take a cigarillo from a box on the table. Moving across the room behind her husband and out onto the veranda, she swayed provocatively. Had he been an artist he could have sketched every curve of her body, Henry thought, as he took a large gulp of rum. Jack Marshall eyed him steadily. Every man has a weakness and maybe, just maybe, he'd found the young Captain Munnerly's. He did not deal in favours but quid pro quo; it usually worked. "Henry, I have a friend, a medical man at the Liverpool Royal Infirmary; a clever fellow. I have some seeds he wants for research. Just seeds." He winked. "Difficult to send though normal channels, get me? Customs are an ignorant bunch, too bloody suspicious. Can you help me out? He'll pay well."

Henry drained his glass and sipped his coffee slowly. He drew long and hard on the cigarillo and turning his head he blew smoke rings, one, two, three, four. He thought of the girl and what might become of her.

As he made his way back to the *Cressida* this night, he followed his usual route. Down the cobbled streets towards the dockside, he could smell the acrid air from oil lamps and ash wood smoke from fires, long since gone out. Little timber shacks leaned close to one another, their timber posts jutting defiantly out into the alleys. Everything was quiet save for a stray dog sauntering along and sniffing for scraps of any kind - but Henry sensed he was being followed and turned quickly. All he could see was a woman leaning against a wall, smoking and coughing, trying to attract his attention. Turning a corner he came to a wide expanse of docks and walked through the moon shadow of the Customs House and past the warehouses. There he felt the fresh salt wind on his face. In a deep breath he caught the tang of seaweed and the detritus that was always floating and slopping against the quayside. The blood surged in his veins when he caught sight of the *Cressida's* dark shape across Havana Bay. She was a magnificent vessel, with the long clean lines of her slim hull sitting low in the water. The three masts so majestic, and the funnel standing proud in the centre… Steam and sail eh? Grandfather was right about that. How he wished he was alive to see her. Henry took little notice of the figure coming towards him; his thoughts were elsewhere. Out of his brooding he acknowledged one thing. He'd have to kill Jacob. That much he owed to Pearl. Humiliation was not enough. Tales would be told, he'd guarantee. There was nothing the men liked better than a damn good fight, especially when a man so much despised was the victim. The figure closed on him. Even in the dim light he could tell by the man's walk he was a sailor: the rolling gait with feet wide apart, so used to the pitch and toss of a moving deck. As he drew level the figure lunged forward, knocking him to the ground.

Henry cursed, 'Damn it man! Look where you're going you drunken sot!' A sharp pain in his ribs now - *must have had a bottle in his hand!* Sure enough at his own side he felt a wetness. He could smell blood, taste it even and rum too. 'The bastard's stabbed me; one of Jacob's men I swear.' Who was he telling, though?

Rising was a struggle… his ship not far ahead. He'd be alright if only he could get help. But his legs buckled beneath him and he slumped back onto the ground, then vomited violently. He crawled away from the pool of sour flux and sat, leaning his back against a barrel. Dizzy and with his mouth open, he gasped for air like a fish in a net flung on the deck to die.

Henry had begun to shiver before he became aware of a hand on his shoulder shaking him forcefully. He turned. "Ramos, what the devil?"

"You O.K. Cap'n Sir, what happen, you sick?"

"Been stabbed. Listen Ramos; get my pipe and bacca, bacca you gave me, here in pocket." Henry lifted his limp arm. "Light it and go to ship, tell night watchman I sent you. Get first mate Morris come here. Go quickly."

Ramos did as Henry ordered and then scuttled off. Henry clenched the pipe between his chattering teeth and inhaled deeply. The dragons tore at his chest until he bellowed out in agony. But as his puffs of smoke became shallower, relief seemed to waft over him. He thought of Caroline and his sons, Arthur and Ralph. Strangely, then, a vision of his grandfather floated before him…

…his birthday had fallen on a Sunday that year, 1879. It was fine and unusually warm. The family set off for St. Peters church in Rock Ferry, as they did each week, filling the oaken pew reserved for the Munnerlys since grandfather George built Havana House and came to live in the locality. After the final, mournful hymn ended the service, they all trooped outside where the vicar stood on the step shaking hands with his parishioners. With his white, wispy hair and pale moon face Henry thought he must be the oldest man he had ever seen. George called across to his daughter-in-law.

"Joan my dear, take the rest of them back to Havana House in the carriages. Henry and I will walk." He put a hand on Henry's shoulder. "Ten today, eh boy?"

"Yes Sir."

"Time you and I had a chat." Henry's cheeks flushed with pride. He supposed this was what grown ups called man to man talk. "Always be proud to be a Munnerly, hold your head up high and be true to yourself. Funny things, families. They make their fortunes and lose them. As the generations continue they make them again, like the ebb and flow of the great river Mersey. You have it in you to make your way in the world, Henry, I can see. You're lucky to be born at this time and in *this city!* Liverpool's flourishing. It's bursting into the future. Be part of it. There's so much happening with - with all these new inventions, engineering projects, trade and commerce.

This city's blessed with men of vision on its shores. Dreams are one thing but *action* is what's needed now. Shipping is the future of this city, I'm certain of it. Do you know they're building steam ships? Can you imagine that, ships without sails? I'll not see it in my lifetime but you will, by God you will. Captain Henry Munnerly, how does that sound. Eh boy? That'd make your grandfather proud, very proud indeed."

"Grandfather, sir, were you a Sea Captain?"

The old man stopped suddenly. His big frame slouched, shoulders slumped and his cheeks reddened. When he sucked in his breath Henry could see the tiny veins on his nose running like purple rivulets and the beads of sweat that broke out on his brow. George Munnerly took out a white handkerchief from his pocket and mopped his face. He coughed so much the dewlap beneath the grey beard wobbled, tight and then loose. "No boy, no, not a Captain but I, we, owned three ships. Fine ships they were too, built on the River Clyde in Glasgow"

"Did you sail in them?" George straightened his stiff body and sighed deeply. Composing himself he gazed at Henry with what must have been an aching heart. *An inquiring mind, the boy has everything; all a man could wish for in a son, but alas not his own.* Disappointment waned as hope welled up in his weary breast. If only he could live long enough to see his ambitions realised and the past forgotten. "Where are they now, those three ships?"

"Sold Henry, sold many years ago. Your father was not interested in ships; no appetite for business you see."

"I am Grandfather. I am."

"I know you are Henry, I know. You'll make the

Munnerlys respected again." George waved his arm in the direction of the city of Liverpool. "Do you remember when I took you to the opening of The Walker? The gallery for all Liverpool's treasures. 1877 it was."

"Yes Sir, I do."

"They were all there Henry, all the city fathers with their ladies in fine clothes, the shipping magnates, the Holts, the Harrisons, the Brocklebanks, the Bibbys, Lord Ismay and Sir Alfred Jones. Ah! Yes, all Liverpool men."

They stopped and George turned to face Henry, putting both hands on his shoulders to say, "Like us. Just one more thing, Henry. Marry a good woman from a respectable family. There are many young fillies in those families I've mentioned. Pick one. Oh, and one very last thing; I'll say to you what your great-grandfather said to me. If it's money you're after, marry it." They walked in silence after that; the grip of the old man's fingers never leaving Henry's shoulder, until they reached Havana's door…

If he was dying he must die with honour, somehow. After all, he came from a proud family, a good family, he always believed. Yet there were some things about their past that he'd pondered over… questions without answers... about money… ships. As a boy his father said he asked too much and then the only response he could hope for was a deep frown from a florid and scowling face… always followed by silence. It was his grandfather had kindled Henry's imagination. The old man spent many hours telling him tales of Irish history and the Fenians. And hadn't he given him his gold watch on his 10th birthday, shortly before he died?

He made up his mind. Many times he'd thought about

how it would be to die like this. If only he had enough strength to drag his near lifeless body to the edge, he could make it over the side. He clasped his cap in his hand and slowly, painfully reached up and placed it on top of the barrel…inside it he placed his gold watch. Morris would find it and know what to do. There was depth beneath the man's melancholy. The two of them understood one another by a look, an expression, a union of minds, no less. Morris would report back to those in Liverpool with due diligence. It was in his nature to ensure that particular facts were not mentioned. He knew the value of a man's self worth. His loyalty was without question; he would carry those secrets to his own grave; that was certain.

His strength was all but run away and his legs were numb, paralysed and heavy. With the last scrap of energy he dragged his useless body to the edge and rolled over. Waves broke around the once strong form, as Henry's arms flailed and yet failed to save him. He gulped the salt water…*Havana Bay…Havana House…* Spluttering he slipped beneath the surface.

The warm Caribbean Sea took him as her own and gently laid him on the sea bed.

from THE LIVERPOOL JOURNAL 0F COMMERCE
February 21st 1902

Obituaries.

It is with deep regret that we announce the death of our esteemed member, Captain Henry Munnerly, Owner/ Master of the "Cressida" in Havana, Cuba on the 26th January. Reports from the Caribbean confirm that Captain Munnerly drowned accidentally whilst making an heroic attempt to save a street urchin, who had been swept into the sea during a violent storm. He dived in immediately, pulling the boy to safety, but in the process appears to have succumbed to a freak wave. Captain Munnerly was a highly respected mariner, known for his seamanship skills, integrity and the promotion of Commercial Relations with the New World. He is survived by his wife Caroline and sons Arthur and Ralph.

Well, why not? Every family needs at least one good apple- mine especially! Sadly, with Henry the seafaring Munnerly's come to an end. There would be no more ships setting out from Liverpool with a Munnerly at the helm. Vessels with names such as the Joan Clarke and the Fair Helena continued to be registered with Lloyds but future generations would remain in Rock Park, watching the city across the Mersey and the Munnerly fortunes that rose and fell with it.

Gold pocket watch, savonette type, once owned by Captain Henry Munnerly.

CHAPTER 5

It was indeed Arthur who'd found this story. He had also written to Linklater and Stewart seeking information about Pearl, the pretext being to make sure that she was well. I thought it more likely that he was curious about a father he had hardly known. No success: that trail was cold and given the upheaval that had taken place in Cuba in more recent times there would seem little chance of tracing any relatives now, assuming any existed.

Various newspaper clippings showed announcements of births, marriages and deaths and an extract from Hansard dated 14th August 1911 which seemed to have had significance... but of course! The Liverpool transport strike that almost brought the country to its knees.

There were a number of other interesting items including two which would have been controversial in their day. A 1918 copy of 'Married Love' by Marie Stopes, one of the original 2000 printed, and its companion work, a small volume on practical birth control, published in 1919, hardly accorded with Nancy's stuffy reputation, indeed they suggested someone rather avant garde. The mystery of the eight year gap in the family was solved and, incidentally, the reason why they had deemed precautions necessary. The number of medical bills, including one from a 'live in' nurse, dating from the time of Florence's birth, suggested that the confinement had been a difficult one.

I moved on to the jewellery box, musty smelling and covered with balding velvet. The contents were wrapped in a piece of silk but a card indicated that it was a gift to Nancy from Arthur on the occasion of their marriage. The necklace and earrings were finely worked pieces in the swirling art nouveau style but the gems were less fine than I would have expected. In previous generations the twining stems and flowers would have been decorated with ruby and emerald rather than the amethyst and peridot that accompanied the small pearls. Clearly things were not going so well by Arthur's time but that was understandable. For two generations Trustees had taken a major role in running the business and the economic climate had changed, with more overseas competitors entering the shipping market.

Suddenly it struck me that there might be another reason for the choice of stones. Green for hope, white for purity and violet for loyalty. The suffragette colours. Nancy had leanings towards female emancipation. It also suggested that her husband knew of her political views and supported them: in contrast to Marie Stopes' husband who had insisted that she give up her membership of the Women's Freedom Party. But the two women had a lot else in common. Both born in the 1880s and married in 1911 but where Nancy's marriage had endured Marie's had ended in annulment. It prompted her to begin her crusade for women's right to control their fertility. To the failure of her contemporary's marriage Nancy probably owed the success of her own, and possibly her life.

These were the things I had found. They confirmed my view of her - and I liked my great grandfather better and better.

Arthur

Only two o'clock. Arthur Munnerly returned the watch to his pocket for what must have been the twentieth time and leaned back against the cushions. Weariness tugged at him like an undertow but he would not yield to it. Convention might prevent him from being with his wife at such a time but the least he could do was to stay awake.

He looked out of the gallery window to where the massive leaves of ancient rhododendrons shaded a billiard table lawn. His mind wandered beyond the stone wall that bordered the property to the river. Its apparent sluggishness was deceptive. There were swift currents and a tidal range of twenty five feet as the water rushed through its narrow mouth, in and out of the Irish Sea - the same sea across which his great grandfather had come a century before. This gateway to a wider ocean had brought the family a fortune - and swallowed Henry Munnerly, his father beneath the warm blue Caribbean.

The present called him back with the sound of the bedroom door opening. Sullivan emerged, heavy face somber. Arthur was on his feet immediately but the doctor did not give him time to speak.

'It's over. The second child was stillborn.'

'And Nancy?' Arthur kept his voice calm although a sick fear gnawed at his stomach.

'Sleeping.'

'Will she- recover?'

Sullivan moved to the mahogany chest of drawers, took out his pen and paper and began to write. A ray of sunlight from the glass dome over the hall fell across his back of his black jacket, catching a myriad of tiny dust motes floating like specks of gold. After a moment he looked up, holding out the note in a stiffly extended hand. His voice was cold with anger. 'Do you care?'

'Of course!' Arthur was horrified that he might think otherwise.

'Then no more babies. I told you that last time.'

'We were careful.'

The doctor snorted. 'Careful! I brought that girl into the world, Munnerly. I was her father's best friend. I don't want to see her dead before her time. Careful isn't good enough. Abstinence is the only certainty. Show some restraint.'

The unfairness of the accusation made Arthur angry. When had anyone ever made Nancy do anything she didn't want to do? Sullivan was still frowning, expecting a response.

'Maybe you're right.' He took a deep breath. 'Does Nancy know about the baby?'

'Not yet.'

'I'll tell her.'

The doctor relented a little. 'Things could be worse. She'll get her strength back in time and you have one healthy daughter.' He fastened his bag. 'I'll call again.'

Arthur watched the older man as he descended, pausing at the bottom to collect his coat and hat. Sullivan was the relic of a past age. Formally dressed no matter how hot the day, a forbidding figure but a good doctor when things were bad, and by all accounts, prepared to waive his fee for those who were unable to afford it.

Reluctantly Arthur made his way along the gallery and stood for a moment outside the bedroom door gathering his courage before turning the handle. Dwarfed by the massive oak four poster, Nancy lay among her pillows, hardly less white than the linen, her normally sleek bob dishevelled and sticky with sweat. Close to her sat the nurse, a tall, solid woman in a blue cotton dress and starched white apron, dark hair confined beneath a severe cap. He could sense her disapproval. Having been present through the interminable hours of labour no doubt she shared Sullivan's opinion.

As he tiptoed across the Persian carpet. Nancy stirred but did not wake. 'Go and have some tea, nurse.'

The woman's chin went up. 'I was told not to leave Mrs Munnerly alone.'

Arthur's tone hardened. 'She won't be alone.'

She rose ponderously, smoothing her apron with exaggerated dignity. 'Dr. Sullivan was very specific....'

'I'll ring if you're needed.' He waited until the door closed before taking the seat beside the bed and lifting Nancy's hand, the fingers felt cold and slack in his. As always he was struck by her fragility. That elegant, slim hipped figure might be the height of fashion but it was far from ideal for motherhood. Sullivan was right. The thought that they must not risk it again was depressing but nothing beside the possibility of losing her.

What a bright, adventurous girl she had been before the Great War. But the influenza epidemic which followed it, had taken first her brothers and then her parents. Then had come the dark times. Nancy had been so obsessed by the need to contact them that she neglected the children and filled the house with a succession of 'sensitives' until the day that one claimed to have seen a middle aged man leap from the gallery to his death in the hall below. That was entirely too close to home. The thought that perhaps the dead might be with them in such a literal sense was far from comfortable and had deterred Nancy from further exploration of 'the beyond'. That in itself showed the extent of the change in her. The girl who had dragged him to that demonstration in 1911 would never have been so easily put off. How ironic that his one and only brush with the law should have been caused by Nancy whom everyone saw as rigid with rectitude.

It had been a year of unrest. A group calling itself the 'Trades Union Federation' had been formed in May and there had been strikes by the seamen's union. Discussions had led to an agreement with the owners which they had promptly broken by importing 'scab' labour and by August the city was rancid with heat and mistrust. With 4000 strikers in the city the authorities had called on the Home Secretary for support which had been granted in generous measure. Some 5,000 troops and more than 2,400 police were at the disposal of the Head Constable. There was even a warship, the Antrim, *anchored* in the river. Liverpool hadn't been under threat of being shelled since the siege by Prince Rupert's troops in the Civil War but Nancy regarded the whole mess as exciting and wanted a closer look. Neither he nor her brother, William had been able to dissuade her. It seemed the lesser evil to go along.

Despite the numbers on St George's plateau, the gathering was orderly. Rows of women and children ranged on the steps of the hall suggested that the strikers intended no violence and there was a respectful hush as speakers, using lorries as platforms, talked of unity and a better deal. Nancy, unrecognisable in borrowed trousers and shirt with her hair tucked under a cap, listened intently. William was clearly bored, frowning and restless. Arthur could hear his muttering, hardly discreet in the middle of a crowd of supporters. For himself, he found an unexpected sympathy with them. It was uncomfortable to realise that he had frittered away more in one night than these families had to live on for a month.

A Captain Tupper had just begun to speak when, out of the corner of his eye, Arthur noticed a disturbance at the point where Lime Street led into the plateau. A moment later men pursued by police surged towards the packed mass of people and ploughed forward. If the fugitives hoped the police would not follow them among the women and children they were mistaken. Both groups piled in to the accompaniment of thuds and screams. Immediately the peaceful assembly broke into warring groups. Arthur caught Nancy's elbow and tried to drag her towards the edge of the crowd but they were carried along by the struggling protagonists as they surged back towards Lime Street. William had disappeared in the melee and someone was shouting over the noise. It came to him that they were reading the Riot Act. The troops were authorised to use live ammunition. He had to get Nancy away.

As soon as there was room he broke into a run, pulling her along after him. From behind came the sound of more skirmishes and ahead, towards Christian Street, he caught the glint of brass on harness and uniforms. Soldiers! He swerved back up Scotland Road and the numbers began to thin out. Another turn took him into a yard behind the rear entrance to the London Hotel. Pressed back against the wall were two men, one in his forties with the broken nose and thickened hands of a seasoned street fighter, the other younger but still powerfully built.

The bigger man stood considering them before motioning to Arthur. 'Best get the girl over the wall.'

Nancy stiffened. 'If you have something to say, please address yourself to me.

'Hoity-toity!' The man grinned. 'Listen Miss, it isn't safe for you here.'

She tossed her head. 'In that case it isn't safe for you either.'

The man nodded without apparent rancour. 'Right enough. Might get a hammerin' but worse might 'appen to you, if you take my meanin'. Best not take the chance.'

Nancy scowled but she stopped arguing and started to climb the wall at the corner of the yard, unceremoniously helped on her way by a big hand placed on her buttocks. Arthur was too taken aback to protest until after the deed was done.

Nancy was scarcely out of sight when the policemen arrived.

There were four of them, solid and bulky in their dark uniforms. Spread across the opening to the entry they seemed threatening but to Arthur the police had always represented order and he felt embarrassed to have run away. He was sure his father, Henry, would not have run, but he told himself that there had been Nancy to consider. Now, however, he could try to be more the man his father would have respected. He stepped forward while the other men watched in disbelief. 'Can I help you, constable?'

The tallest officer, fair with an impressive moustache, smirked unpleasantly. ''Quite the gent ain't 'e?'

Another officer prodded Arthur with his baton who backed up until he found himself with nowhere to go.

'Too full of 'isself by 'arf'

'You're making a mistake, constable. I'm Arthur Munnerly of the shipping line of that name.'

The first man's eyes swept over him. 'Vallee on 'is day off is 'e?'

Only now did Arthur recall how he was dressed. The frayed striped shirt and worn corduroys did nothing to support his claim but he had no choice but to try to convince them.

'I didn't want to stand out.'

'Done a good job then!' The man chuckled at his own joke. 'You're under arrest.'

Arthur drew himself up to his full five feet ten. 'On what charge?'

This time the baton met his ribs hard. He bent forward gasping. Taking advantage of the distraction his two companions attempted to force a way past but the police were ready for them and the melee closed around him. The constables lashed out ferociously and Arthur heard the dull thud as wood met flesh but the police weren't having it all their own way. There were grunts and cries on both sides. Before he had recovered his breath he saw a baton descending towards his head and instinctively threw up his arm to fend it off.

A loud crack and a blinding pain and everything below his elbow became useless. Sick and dizzy from shock he was dragged towards the police wagon. He tried to break free but they shoved him into the van and slammed the door.

It was filled with other bodies and suffocatingly hot. There was the smell of sweat, stale beer and tobacco. His arm hurt abominably and he used his good hand to hold it across his body to protect it from further damage. He fought the urge to throw up. Thank God Nancy hadn't been caught. Voices, raised in dispute, penetrated his consciousness and he realised that he was the subject.

'Reckon what 'e said about being a Munnerly were true?'

'Might be. Them 'ands ain't never done any work.'

The van drew to halt and the doors were thrown open to reveal grimy red brick walls and a stout door. Policemen stood to either side, funnelling the prisoners through into the cells. Arthur remained leaning against the wall as the others clambered out. Binney, Nancy's helper, also hung back. 'This lad's 'urt.'

The police sergeant peered inside. ''E'll be alright.'

'Needs a doctor.'

'Get 'im inside.'

Binney shrugged. 'Come on lad. I'll give yer 'and.'

Arthur leaned against him, careful of the arm. 'Nancy'll tell my family. They'll get us out.'

' 'Ope it's that easy.'

His memories of the night were hazy. Pain from his arm made sleep impossible and by the time help arrived, in the form of Nancy's father with a note from the Head Constable, he was feverish and confused but insistent that Binney and the others should also be released. That had proved unachievable but Nancy's father had, himself, represented the men in court ensuring that they were fined rather than jailed and the money had been provided. In fact the whole city was anxious to put the matter behind it. More than a hundred people had been injured and general opinion was that the police drafted in from other areas had over-reacted. Still, it had made up his mind about Nancy. With the blessings of both sets of parents they had been married just before Christmas that same year.

Nancy's hand gripped his more firmly and she opened her eyes. The look in them, in that unguarded moment, was little short of panic. Arthur leaned forward to put his arms round her and she buried her face against his shoulder.

'I'm sorry, Arthur.'

The muffled words took him by surprise. 'You've no reason to be sorry.'

'I've lost our baby.'

He drew her closer. 'I haven't lost you. And we have a healthy girl.'

Nancy pulled away. 'Is she? Let me see.'

He detached himself carefully and peered into the cradle. The round, snub nosed face of his latest daughter stared back with that unfocused yet somehow knowing look that all new born babies share. He bundled the infant and handed her to his wife.

'She's beautiful.'

Nancy studied the child thoughtfully, a small smile hovering about her lips. 'I hope she improves before the christening.'

He sat down on the edge of the bed and held out his finger. The baby's eager mouth fastened on to it, sucking greedily. 'She's hungry'

'I dare say.'

'Aren't you going to feed her?'

'No. It's too much- and there are perfectly adequate substitutes.'

It was not a good sign but understandable. Nancy had lost so many people that she loved. The refusal to allow herself to become attached even to her own children was a form of self preservation. Perhaps if he didn't press too hand she would change her mind. 'Have you decided on a name?'

She nodded. 'Margery. Yes, I think so. Time to break with the past. The world's changing. She'll have the vote, a career, travel.'

'As you wish my dear.' It wasn't a name he much cared for but, since Nancy had suffered to produce the child, it seemed only fair that she should choose the name. He saw her smile, conscious of having got her own way.

'You know, Arthur, I'm rather hungry too.'

'I'll get cook to send up some broth.'

The smile became mischievous. 'I need red meat Arthur, not a bowl of slop! And half a bottle of the claret. Get that horrible nurse to bring it, and some milk for the baby.'

Delighted to see signs of recovery, Arthur was up in a moment. He closed the door behind him and almost skipped down the stairs before he realised that four pairs of worried eyes were watching him from the hallway. He looked at his family with some pride. Tom, at thirteen, was trying to feign unconcern. (He'd been planning to have a talk with the boy but perhaps there was nothing left to say). Then there was Edward, two years younger- and then the girls, Georgina and Florence, pretty in their flounced dresses, alike enough to be twins with barely twelve months between them.

He arranged his face into a smile. 'Cheer up. Mama's well and you have a new sister. Margery Munnerly is with us.'

After Arthur I was presented with a dilemma. Ralph, his younger brother, had been killed at Ypres in the Great War and any letters he may have written were missing...and I had a strong suspect for the thief. (My own father!) Anyway, had I followed my original plan I should have progressed to my grandmother, Margery, now. But some of the things left behind showed that some of Nancy's children had a story worth telling. Although it meant that my story would become more complex I could not justify excluding any of them. I debated the order in which they should be told and decided that rather than dealing with them in order of birth I would do exactly the opposite which meant that the second son, Edward, who died during the World War Two, should come first, then Great Uncle Tom whom I remembered well, and Great Aunt Florence last.

As it turned out this was an excellent decision.

I liked what I knew of Edward. As a boy he seemed to have been spontaneous and outgoing but with an affectionate and caring nature. He liked animals and sports and, in his teens, had sailed regularly with the Royal Mersey Yacht Club both on the family boat and crewing for other members. The sea seemed to be in his blood so it was no wonder that when war came he had chosen the Navy, although enlisting as an ordinary seamen was an odd choice when education, background and experience might well have justified his entering as an officer.

His choice of marriage partner also seemed to have come as a surprise to the family and not a welcome one, particularly to his mother. That might have been why they chose to live in a Liverpool terrace rather than in Havana House, which could easily have accommodated them. Unlike Arthur and Nancy who seemed to relish being photographed, of Edward and

Frances there was a single, badly damaged, snapshot. Edward in uniform and Frances in a pale suit with a neat little hat and gloves. It might have been their wedding day, because I couldn't find any other pictures. Sad that they had so little time together.

If there was friction, his letters, in beautiful copperplate writing, gave no sign of it. They say nothing directly concerning his ship or its whereabouts but he was adept at giving hints. In one letter, dated 14th February 1944 and signed '*with love and kisses*' he wrote '*I hope it's a little warmer for you than it is here but I suppose I'm not so far away as to make a great difference.*' At that time he was on patrol in the Western Approaches between Bristol and the English Channel, escorting merchant ships to their rendezvous points where the convoys were mustered. It also mentions that his brother-in-law (Georgina's husband) had been torpedoed twice but had escaped unscathed and was home on leave. Edward would not be so lucky. He had only six days to live.

I imagined what it must have been like to have someone in the services, never to be sure whether you had seen them for the last time - to receive a telegram like this one, still in its tiny brown envelope.

'The Admiralty regrets to inform you that Leading Steward Edward Munnerly is missing in action, presumed killed on Sunday 20th February 1944 when the ship on which he was serving, H.M.S. Warwick, was sunk in an enemy action. A letter will follow.'

Nancy and Arthur Munnerly pictured on one of the many Continental trips they took between the wars. The caption on the reverse is barely legible but probably reads 'St Malo, August 1936'

CHAPTER 6

H.M.S. Warwick

The Destroyer *H.M.S. Warwick* was launched on 28th December 1917 and commissioned into service with the Royal Navy on the 18th March 1918, just in time to serve out the remaining months of World War 1. Almost immediately Warwick distinguished herself in the famous Zeebrugge raid, acting as the flagship for Admiral of the Fleet Lord Roger Keyes. Interestingly, this was the raid at which the Liverpool Ferry boats *Iris* and *Daffodil* played a vital role in blocking the harbour and earned the right to use the title 'Royal'. When war ended, *Warwick* remained in service until 1935 when she joined the reserve fleet.

In 1939 *Warwick* was brought back into service and on 16th September that year, only two weeks after the outbreak of World War 2, she rescued the surviving crew members of the first British Merchant ship to be sunk, bringing them back to Liverpool. During August 1940 *Warwick* rescued the master and 28 members of the crew of the merchantman *Ampleforth,* returning them also to Liverpool.

The final and probably most noble of these actions took place on 3rd July 1942 when *Warwick* picked up rescued crew members of the American tanker *Gulfbelle,* which had been torpedoed and badly damaged. Despite the enormous risks involved Warwick took the tanker in tow and delivered it safely to Port of Spain, Trinidad.

But luck runs out for the old lady on 20th February 1944. *H.M.S. Warwick* is off Trevose Head, North Cornwall when she is torpedoed.

Edward

1944: in a war that seemed never-ending, good news was scarce, especially when it arrived in small brown envelopes marked *OHMS.* Husbands, sons and lovers were all caught up in the deadly game. Wives, mothers and daughters had to take the roles of their menfolk in the struggle for survival and for the victory some were destined never to see.

The telegram was addressed to *Leading Steward E.Munnerly.* Frances, his bride of just a few months, looked down at the slight figure in Post Office uniform and a pillbox hat held to his head at a crazy angle by a tight chinstrap. She handed over a silver threepenny piece.

'Thank you very much, ma'am. Good morning.'

The tiny figure disappeared as quickly as he had arrived.

Frances closed the door and stood for a moment frowning at the envelope before taking it through to the kitchen. Edward, still in his pyjamas, was at the table enjoying the last days of an all-too-short leave. He looked surprised. 'That for me?'

Frances handed him the envelope. 'Wouldn't it be nice if it just said the war's over! You could stay where you are!'

'Never mind. Won't be long now and what a helluva

party we're going to throw when that happens.' He raised his eyebrows as he read. 'Report *HMS Warwick* 0800 hours, Wednesday 2nd February 1944, Wapping Dock, Liverpool. Signed, Draft Commander, Western Approaches HQ.' Putting on a brave face, he turned towards Frances. 'Well, at least I don't have so far to go this time. It's only a tram ride and a five-minute walk.' He saw tears welling up in her eyes. A lump began to rise in his own throat. He couldn't bear to see her upset.

'Blast it.' Unusually, Frances blurted out her feelings. 'Only the second time I've seen you since we got married-now they're dragging you away again.' She felt the comfort of his arms wrapping around her as the tears started to flow. 'God, Edward, it's not fair.' Her voice trembled with emotion. 'What if something happened to you? What would I do?'

'Don't worry. It won't be long now. We've got them on the run. The end's getting closer every day. Maybe six months or even sooner and I'll be home forever. And I promise I'll never leave you again. Must get dressed now.'

He slipped quietly upstairs, reappearing ten minutes later in his navy uniform. 'Come on, my love, we've got all today untouched. Let's not waste it.'

Frances looked at him in an almost childish way. 'Teddy, it's snowing a blizzard out there.'

But he had no intention of letting the last day of his leave pass unnoticed. 'We'll catch the tram into town and find something to do. Might see a newsreel and some cartoons at the Tatler.'

Half an hour later they *were* on the tram into the city centre, Frances's arm tightly linked through his. At least the air raids had stopped for the time being, though some roads were still impassable, covered with rubble from the bombing. They walked hand in hand past the remains of Blacklers' store, then Lewis's, before crossing back through Clayton Square and arriving at C and A Modes, now operating only on a ground floor extended by the use of tarpaulins. The navy uniform did the trick and Frances left the shop with a cotton floral, patterned dress regarded as something of a luxury in the circumstances. Hardly winter wear but there was little choice.

That night they lay in each others' arms and prayed.

Wednesday came all too soon. After a tearful farewell Edward had to catch the seven o'clock tramcar in the morning, which went only as far as Castle Street. At the bottom of James Street, he turned left towards the Wapping and Albert Docks, each depressing step taking him further from Frances. From the road he could make out the shape of the Destroyer *Warwick* lying alongside the jetty. He'd seen her on odd occasions while on convoy escort duties in the North Atlantic, but only from a distance. *Warwick* had a good reputation, never having lost a single one of the ships in her care on the convoy routes.

With a salute to the quarterdeck Edward faced the duty officer. 'Leading Steward Munnerly reporting for duty, sir.'

The portly little officer's head snapped around at the cultivated accent. He studied a sheet of paper. 'We're expecting you. Mess deck FX4, just forward of midships. Claim your bunk, then report to Petty Officer Johnson.'

'Aye, aye, sir.'

Edward was familiar with the ship's general layout. Accommodation on board was cramped. Two sets of three-tier bunk beds lined the bulkheads, with six grey steel lockers for personal effects. In reality it was a single cabin converted in wartime to accommodate six men. Outside in the passageway stood six narrow steel wardrobes and two rows of shoe racks. Oilskins for heavy weather and greatcoats for the cold, *darknights* belonged in the wardrobes, and rubber sea-boots on the shoe racks. Nothing wet was allowed in the cabin, and no footwear at all – the Navy's way of fighting tuberculosis. Edward guessed that nothing had changed on this ship since it was first commissioned halfway through World War One, except perhaps that the crew's numbers had doubled. He was cheered, at least, to discover that *Warwick* often visited Liverpool on her convoy escort duties. He might even get a 48-hour pass and slip home for a day or two. It was a possibility…

HMS Warwick moved out on a frisky six o'clock tide and on across the breakwater on a course she had taken many times before. Once in the Irish Sea she headed north into a heavy swell, struggling to make headway in wintry conditions. Her forecastle seemed to slice through the waves, making them divide and then re-converge as they crashed down on to the bridge. No one was allowed on deck, all hatches being secured. Edward quickly settled into his duties, but as the weather eased he found himself being called to action stations frequently until the crew were up to speed in their response time. Everyone had at least two jobs, one of which would always be an action station duty.

Two days later their first task began: to round up the stragglers of a huge convoy that had crossed the Atlantic with only a few losses. Off the west coast of Ireland the convoy divided into smaller groups. Several destroyers were on hand to act as escorts and lead the way to the ships' respective home ports. *Warwick,* naturally, led those destined for Liverpool, dashing up and down the line at speed to ensure that no surprise attack took place. Any submarine in the vicinity would recognise the tactic and run silently till the danger was past. But there was none: in a week to the day, she was to tie up again at Wapping Dock ready to refuel and sail again to escort an outgoing convoy now gathering in Liverpool Bay.

Edward managed only a 24 hour release from duty and that with strict orders to be back on board before five o'clock. Unable to phone Frances, he headed straight for home, but she had already left for her work at the Royal Ordnance factory. Jumping a number 22 tram to Long Lane, Aintree and walking to the factory, he noticed nothing of his home town, intent on one thing, one dear face. His desperation was enough to persuade an armed guard at the factory entrance to contact her. But by the time they met the hour they were allowed together had been reduced to forty-five minutes. He watched as Frances disappeared from view, then walked slowly back to the tram stop, 'We'll be together again, my love,' he'd whispered, unaware that others had different plans.

The German submarine, the *U413*, had been lying on the sea bed outside Newquay harbour, undetected for several days during that month. *Kapitan* Gustave Poel, its commander, waited with nerves stretched almost to breaking point. To be discovered would be to bring a deluge of depth charges raining down on him and almost certain death. Through his code machine – the very same that the British would name Enigma - German intelligence kept him informed of the movements of any merchant ships shortly to arrive off Trevose Head near Padstow. This was the final most dangerous leg of a journey which had brought them across the Atlantic. If this intelligence were correct one group would shortly sight their home port of Bristol. The rest would steer a northerly course to Liverpool. Poel's mission was to ensure that as few as possible arrived at their final destination. The U-boat's voyage from the submarine pens at Brest in northern France had not been without incident. Four times they had been obliged to surface to change the vessel's air, using night as their cover. Twice they had carried out emergency diving procedures to avoid the attention of patrolling British warships.

On the morning of Sunday, 20th February, the boat moved slowly into an attacking position between her targets and the shoreline. The first of the merchant ships was due in the area later that day. So far surprise had worked in the Germans' favour.

Poel checked his position, then gave orders to ascend to periscope depth. Once there, he couldn't believe his luck. Within periscope range lay two British destroyers and several coastal fishing boats. The choice was stark: either he could dive again and await for the imminent arrival of the merchant ships, or he could join battle now, outnumbered, against a well-armed enemy. For a while he pondered, then decided. He would attack the larger of the two warships, both of which seemed preoccupied with the fishing vessels. The advantage of surprise was still with him. Almost certainly they would not expect an attack from the shore side.

He smelt the crew's sweat as he called them to action

stations. The destroyer would be a prize worth an honour if they succeeded, far more valuable than a merchant ship or two.

In Newquay, that Sunday morning was typically wintry. People walked briskly, trying to keep their circulation active on the way to church. Voices would soon be raised in prayer and hymns – *'For those in peril on the sea,'* among others. The air-sea rescue team at the nearby St Merryn Fleet Air Arm base had passed an undisturbed morning and were preparing to stand down for lunch.

At 11.42 am Poel gave the order to fire the first torpedo. He watched the tell-tale streak of white foam as it headed away on its killing vector. The aim was unerring.

On the target ship's bridge three officers are on duty. First comes Commander Denis Rayner, DSC, RNVR, the captain. He has another twenty-five years to look forward to. Standing alongside him is Lieutenant David Harries, the navigating officer. He has a long, fruitful forty years to live. With him is Sub-Lieutenant Peter Whinney, recently married. He has just under an hour.

11.43 am. Petty Office Telegraphist William Porter is about to leave his office to go below for lunch. Within a minute he is forced to return and begin sending out distress calls to be picked up at the Fleet Air Arm base. He has less than three minutes on earth.

11.44 am. An acoustic torpedo strikes the ship's hull with a violent explosion. For two minutes William Porter sends out his Mayday in Morse code signals. They are all that remains to him before a second explosion rips the ship apart and the ammunition hold receives a direct hit.

11.46 am. Lieutenant Harries destroys all his secret charts. The ship is sinking fast. The three officers slide down her side from the bridge and swim for their lives. They have only a couple of minutes to distance themselves from the hull and the lethal downward suction of the dying ship.

11.47 am. *Warwick* has vanished under the waves, taking many of the crew with her. The scene is strangely calm. It is as if the great ship had never existed.

But another deadly enemy begins to appear and to extinguish those few survivors still afloat in the freezing water. Thick black oil from fractured tanks is rising to the surface and spreads rapidly, finding it way into unprotected eyes, mouths, throats, stomachs. The living and the dead float together in its blackness, impossible to tell apart. In the next hour more give up their lives. One of them will be Edward Munnerly. The face of his wife, beloved in its various moods…memories of the dear and quarrelsome clan from which he springs…images of the handsome/ugly house still solid, still standing, immortal it seems amongst the greenery of Rock Park, all slipping away one by one….

Poel watches, presumably with satisfaction as the torpedo struck its target. He notes the scene, mentally preparing the day's entry in his log. For a second he considers taking the fight to *HMS Scimitar* but thinks better of it: shortly, a massive search would be launched to find and destroy his vessel. He gives the order to dive.

Once deep below the waves he turned south. He takes a course heading them back across the Channel to the safety of Brest and refuelling.

Frances Munnerly answered the knock at her front

door within seconds. It was the same, ruddy-faced, little telegraph boy.

'I'm sorry, Mr Munnerly's not here today.'

The boy gazed up at her. He appeared if anything even smaller than before, seen from her position at the top of two doorsteps. 'This one's for Mrs Frances Munnerly.' He held out the usual brown envelope, its front stamped *OHMS*.

She tugged out the telegram. 'Maybe he's coming home on leave.' But as she held up the ticker-tape message her hand began to shake uncontrollably.

The Admiralty regrets…

More than an hour passed before she could bring herself to walk to the telephone at the corner of the road.

'It's for you, Florence. It sounds like Edward's wife.'

Georgina handed her sister the phone, then listened. (No doubt that new girl, Annie, would be lurking somewhere close, ears pricked). What was this about, then? Were they short of money, wanting a loan? There seemed no other reason why Frances should ring.

'Hello. What can I do for you?'

As the distant, faint voice dissolved into sobbing the thought came to Florence, strange yet moving, that the first thoughts of this woman, Frances, had been less for herself than for Edward's family.

After Edward (my great uncle) came those members of the family that I had known personally, although not well. Because Margery was much younger than the rest they had all seemed very elderly. I was closest to Great Aunt Georgina. She often ended up baby sitting me. She was very sweet - and I missed her when she died, more than I miss my own father.

Havana House was an odd household. The four siblings were all in residence and there was a floating population of Grandma Margery's friends and acquaintances, all self styled artists: I recall a bearded young man wandering around declaiming his latest poems without a stitch on. It didn't bother me and Grandma took it in her stride but it caused a tremendous row with Great Aunt Flo, who threatened to call the police. She would have done it too. Respectability was as important to her as life itself...

The last of the four, Great Uncle Tom, had taken a suite of rooms at the top of the house, which included the little observatory with its dome and telescope. Often he did not bother to come down even for meals. Retired by then, he had been a respected architect and still received occasional commissions despite his advanced age. He was a man of strong, if contained, passions, completely absorbed by his work - and still incandescent about the by-pass which had bisected Rock Park some years before leaving the properties on the river side of the road almost marooned.

I hate to think what he would have to say if he saw it now, with the houses divided into flats and the walkway which ran alongside the water neglected and no longer safe to use.

HMS Warwick

In 1984 those survivors of the Warwick still alive attended a Reunion and a Memorial Service at St Merryn's Church, Padstow for their lost shipmates.

CHAPTER 7

To our family, as to most others, the war did much harm, taking Edward and both his brother-in-laws.

In the autumn of 1939 the British Government - fearing spies and enemy agents - completed something called The National Register. All citizens were on it and had to be issued with ID cards. Considering with whom we were at war, Germans and Austrians were going to be treated with real suspicion. The press ran a campaign under the heading 'Intern the Lot'. Coastal areas were thought to be at particular risk so 'aliens' were moved away from them. This applied even to 'Class C' refugees- mostly Jewish people, many of whom had fled the Nazis. Many members of Liverpool's Jewish community were interned on the Isle of Man. But for others the only choice was a long and perilous voyage to far flung parts of the Dominions.

But why should all this have anything to do with the Munnerlys...?

Tom

The more I read the papers, the less I comprehend
The world and all its capers, and how it will all end.
Nothing seems to be lasting, but that isn't our affair;
We've got something permanent, I mean in the way we care....

Tom Munnerly loves a good song and tonight's Gershwin concert should be full of them. He loves this Philharmonic Hall too. With its yellow walls and art deco figures, the auditorium still reminds him of a Greek fable. No doubt about it, its architect, Rowse, was clever. And Tom has a lot to thank him for. As a fresh young member of his firm, he and the sculptor Edmund Thompson worked on much of its detail. It's what took him from promising student to successful architect: made a man of him. Well maybe not – the war did that - and meeting Sophie. Tonight, under its shell-shaped ceiling of curves and concealed lights, the audience waits as eagerly as he does for the sounds and rhythms that will soon flood every corner...

For once, the orchestra has forgone its drab evening dress. The men sport white tuxedos and the women in an unbridled range of colours add a splash of glamour, an essential glitz. For that was how it had seemed in the Thirties, for the lucky few – a time of fun and new found freedoms. True, behind the scenes, Liverpool struggled: America's Depression saw to that. Dwindling numbers of ships leaving for other shores: things could only get worse.

Not that the poor noticed. One day's deprivation was like any other. But his sort; the Munnerlys, who read the papers, they'd understood. And they ignored it; kept up the pretence. With their parties and concerts, dinners and cocktails, time passed, as it always had, in splendid fashion. But for the war, who knows how things might have turned out? Best not go back down that route, he tells himself, as the lights dim. To an ebullient round of applause, the portly singer takes the stage and the conductor, his place on the podium.

It's very clear our love is here to stay;

With the opening phrase and the mellow seductive tones of the baritone, Tom feels a familiar surge of longing. Good tunes do that of course – evoke times that are fresh and open for the pleasanter things – like love between two young people, like him and Sophie…

She was unlike the local girls. There was a remoteness amounting to diffidence which at first he found as foreign as her

German accent. Though to be fair, her English was fluent. Slim, with that heavy black hair, dark eyes and pale face, so typical of her Jewish race, she stood apart from the others in the front row of the sopranos. She seemed composed; serene. He'd felt nervous asking her out: intimidated by her intelligence and the searching look she gave him as he struggled for the right words. Only later, when the two of them were alone, did he discover her lighter side. Her laughter was infectious, like her presence, vivid. It was as if she hadn't a care in the world.

Not for a year, but ever and a day....

Over that first cup of tea, he'd bombarded her with questions. It was as if once he found the courage, there was no stopping him. How long had she been here: how had she got in: weren't only those with jobs like servants or nurses, allowed to stay? "I'm lucky", she said. "It was easier then. And Papa has friends here, Mark and Adele. Thanks to them, I teach a little music at a school in Hope Place and I live nearby in Pilgrim Street – do you know it?"

He did of course, and why it had that name. Like so many Liverpool streets, there was a story behind it. He'd tell her one day. Not yet though. Those early seafaring days of the likes of the Munnerlys would take some explaining...

"Now you," she said. "What made you an architect? Have you always loved buildings?"

He supposed he had. It started with his family home, Havana House, built to embrace the dazzling stretch of water between it and Liverpool's shore. An elegant front of brick and stone, its massive red chimneys and Welsh slate roof changed from greenish yellow on wet November days to a magical blue in summer. How boldly its jagged shadows reached across the terrace. And how stark, the contrast between them and Havana's interior staircase that rose from ground to attic in a series of seemingly endless spirals.

"As stark," she'd asked, "as this Philharmonic Hall?"

He hadn't thought of it like that. She had a point though.

Certainly the transition from something like Havana to Rowse's brave new vision could be viewed as monumental.

Among Havana's treasures on the first floor gallery hung the Munnerly family painting. Each evening and morning, as he passed by, he'd check all the children were present and correct. The girls, so aloof in their draperies, stood poised as if to dance against a background of ships leaving for foreign lands. Beside them, their brother looked on with an air of slight impatience, as if waiting for something better. As routinely as the hours that struck on the clock nearby, Tom set his days against this novel arrangement of unknown ancestors. When he heard by what means it had come into existence, he'd wondered at its mere removal from pride of place to this subdued area of the first floor gallery. One day, he vowed, when Havana belonged to him, the painting would be returned.

He told Sophie none of this: only how he discovered by chance in his father's library, a slim volume of Bauhaus architecture. How, from its angular simplicity, so reminiscent of Havana's shadows, it seemed a natural progression to the delights of Art Deco where every detail had to earn its place. And how fired with enthusiasm, alongside meticulous studies of Havana's decor, he'd produced his own alternatives.

"What did your family think- did they like them?"

Like, he'd explained, was a word not used much by the Munnerlys. Nancy found them 'unusual'; and Arthur had questioned their purpose. Impossible of course to explain to either of them how on each new sheet any and everything was possible and because of that, the world and his future looked decidedly rosy.

Sophie smiled knowingly. She seemed to understand. So much so, he'd almost told her how things looked even rosier now, with her beside him. That like the words in the song, it was becoming clear; surprisingly clear that for him, anyway, *love*, if such a thing existed of course, was quite likely *here to stay*.

Instead, he'd said, "They're showing Hitchcock's *The Lady Vanishes* at the Forum: would you like to go?"

"I'd love to. Shall I dress up?"

"Oh no," he'd said a little too hastily.

The radio and the telephone and the movies that we know,
May just be passing fancies and in time may go....

There was no *passing fancy* about that night. After the film, they'd dined at Reeces. In a deep red dress with black beads around her neck, she looked so good he'd hoped his friends would turn up after all. They hadn't. But she had a letter to show him.

"Your mother writes often?"

"Yes. Otherwise she thinks she'll forget something."

"You seem very close?"

"We have to be. On Fridays everyone meets at the Synagogue; to worship and after, have a wonderful time. Sunday's your day, isn't it?"

The comparison seemed tenuous. True, after the service, various relatives came back for lunch, to talk a lot; argue too. But over the years, several had died, or emigrated. These days such occasions were confined to weddings and funerals.

"That's so sad Tom! You should come to the synagogue one day to see what it is like. Yes?"

He'd nodded; imagined telling his family about it. The fallout would be huge. Arthur might understand; but Nancy? She had plans of her own for him. Mixing with Jews on the Sabbath or any other day would not be part of them.

"Still," Sophie insisted; "as a family, you must have fun together."

Certainly they all attended the dances at the Town Hall just as they had, before the fire, the concerts at the Philharmonic. But fun? Real conversation was always sparing… and, while there were the odd games of Newmarket or whist with Edward and the girls, they tended to end on a row, with one of his sisters, usually Margery, going off in a huff; so fun? No.

By June, work on the Hall was finished. Such comings and goings there had been: what with the meetings between committee and corporation: the delays, threats and counter threats. With that last minute postponement in April, everyone feared the Hall would yet again be sabotaged by the political whims of one side or the other.

At St George's Hall, he heard her play for the first time. Beethoven's trios: it was extraordinary; he'd shut his eyes, unable to believe the strength of her playing. And after, they had strolled through St John's Gardens towards the Old Haymarket and the Queensway tunnel. "What do you think?" he'd asked with barely concealed pride.

"It's a bit like a marble fortress or castle, isn't it? The arch could be its entrance and the road, the moat around it?"

He pointed to the clean white lines of the parapet, etched against the darkening sky. "See below it, the sculpture with the two bulls?"

"Just about. They're very slender for bulls aren't they? From here, they look more like winged horses or even Jaguars?"

"They're meant to. They represent the tunnel's swift and heavy traffic."

At that, she'd burst out laughing. Waves of laughter, noisy and energetic had ricocheted off the alabaster walls and echoed deep into the tunnel. Dismayed, he'd waited for her to finish. "I'm sorry," she'd said at last; "they're very beautiful bulls." More giggles. "And stylish too"-

"But what?"

"It's just that for all their gallant efforts, the road's quite empty. See! There isn't a vehicle anywhere!"

"It's quiet now", he'd said. "You should have been here for its opening! Everywhere, masses of people: on benches, leaning out of windows, up on the roofs. The police and armed forces keeping order and just there, not five yards from where we're standing, King George V, no less, watched the proceedings. And only a handful of us knew what it looked like behind its heavy curtains."

She'd turned to him then, and put her arms tight around his neck, kissed him full on the lips. He felt torn between his flood of desire for her and guilt at what he'd just been thinking. So what if she was different? Nancy and Arthur would understand. They'd see how delightful she could be. It was just a matter of time.

"I'm sorry if I offended you. It must have been exciting," she'd whispered in his ear.

"It was, but not as exciting as with you now."

And in the dark, he'd meant it. With the scent of her skin and the softness of her hair against his face, he had no doubt she was the girl for him.

If only everything else had been as straightforward. With war never far away, things were getting ugly and not just in London. Liverpool too had its Fascists. Letters to the press damned the increased arrivals of stateless Jews from Germany as *outrageous.* He wanted Sophie to meet the family, but how sensible in the circumstances, was that? Maybe he should wait a week or so; let things quieten down?

They hadn't though. And however he looked at it; with the gulf growing ever wider, what chances of the two families coming together now?

But oh my dear, our love is here to stay....

And at last here they were, on June 19th, in Box 18, sitting with Rowse and those same grudging dignitaries, listening to the speeches of those who counted. Momentarily, she'd snuggled up to him. "It's wonderful, isn't it? Such elegant lights; and look at the way the pillars and boxes curve right the way round; we could be inside a huge ship or luxury hotel. I can't wait to show Mama and Papa – they'll be so impressed, and even more so with the concerts."

The new hall's first concert the following night was full of songs too. He'd sat in the box for the first half alone – watched Sophie and the chorus perform Handel's *Solomon.* In the interval he'd waited upstairs in the foyer, by Edmund's gold relief; impatient for her to emerge from the mass of concert goers.

She'd looked elated. For a moment, he'd felt oddly jealous of her. Listening to music was all very well, but how much grander it must be to be a part of it. To be able to stand up with so many different people and recreate as one voice those miraculous sounds, plucked as if from the air by composers like Mozart and yes, Handel too – though not perhaps this piece?

"What did you think?" she'd asked.

"It could be more cheerful...that verse about hopeless love; not to mention death and wild despair. I'd rather sit here and look at Edmund's Apollo. It's brilliant, isn't it the way he has him charming the birds and animals?"

Sophie shrugged her shoulders.

He'd said, "I tell you what, when Edmund designs our panel-"

"What panel?"

"The one I've commissioned for you and me."

"You never told me-"

"Well I'm telling you now."

After the concert, they'd danced till late to the music of the Ambassadors. She told him of her life in Berlin. "It was so simple then. Everyone was happy. Papa was a brilliant doctor and Mama's soirees were the highlight of the week. Music was everywhere. In the summer, we went with friends to Carlsbad - but you know about that."

"When did it change?"

"Gradually… Papa was forbidden to practise any more…then, after Kristellnacht," Sophie's voice faltered, Tom held her tight.

He remembered Kristellnacht. The news on the radio was full of it. Shops, businesses and even synagogues had been destroyed and huge numbers arrested and imprisoned. His family sat transfixed; unable to comprehend. After, everyone resumed breakfast as if nothing had happened. He could hear Nancy's voice now, as she reminded him again of his duty as a Munnerly to partner that frumpy Heather to the Cunard dance. Tom had left the room in a fury. And to think while that was going on, Sophie had sat alone in her room, despairing. Well from now on, he would be there to look after her....

"Funny," he'd said.

"What is?"

"These songs they're playing-"

"Love songs you mean?"

"Not so long ago I'd have seen them as silly. Now…" he'd held her closer and gently kissed the lobe of her left ear.

"What, Tom?"

"There's something to them after all!"

It's very clear… Signs of war were everywhere. The heat-wave was relentless and Hitler's threats hung like clouds over the city. One day they'd met early; wandered along the quayside and found a cool place to sit... The sun shone in a blameless sky; it should have been a perfect day, but for Sophie. He watched a large tear slide down her cheek and into her ice-cream.

"You've heard from home?"

"Yes. I can't believe it. We can't even make music at home any more."

"What do you mean? Who can't?"

"We can't! Jews are forbidden to play – first it's public concerts and opera; now it's not at all. Mama's beside herself. They took Mendelssohn's statue away – the Nazis are taking everything from us – even our souls."

"It won't last. Hitler will be forced out."

"Will he? Mama says it's getting worse. They're everywhere - groups of them, singing loudly; in the streets. And they say they love music – what music? Well something good's come from it. Papa's convinced at last, home and possessions don't matter now. They're ready to leave."

"I've had some news too. My call up papers: I'm to report this Friday."

"Oh, Tom! What's happening? It's as if the world's turned upside down – all our lovely times together, gone forever?"

He wanted more than anything to take her in his arms, wave a magic wand and banish all thoughts of war – instead, he'd stood back, aware of his own fear, like cold steel that struck the depths of his stomach. His voice, part anxious, part teasing was that of a stranger. "It's tough, but we'll get through it. I'll be back and then there'll be other times."

"Will there?"

"Of course, I promise!"

"And by then I'll have been to London and Mr Hoechst will have sorted out Mama and Papa. You're right Tom; I'm being silly. Of course everything will work out – what matters is that we're together."

There was that optimism again, that unswerving certainty. Was it enough though? How easily would her family settle? Really the situation should be no different to that of his ancestors. Suppose they'd been forced back to Ireland? What of the Munnerly fortune then? Havana House would never have existed. "I've been thinking; let's have a grand evening out together? I mean with my parents and yours too, once they're here? We could book a table at the Adelphi?"

Sophie's smile was pure delight. "They will love you and look on you as one of their own." *Together we're going a long, long way....*

The night before he'd left, Nancy had put on a bit of a celebration.

"Nonsense", she'd said when he'd protested. "Besides it's not just for you; there's Edward too. It can't be long before…" She stiffened, as was her way. "Having a few friends round was your father's idea – if you feel that strongly, you should speak to him about it!"

With the party in full flow, he'd slipped away; dialled and

listened to the rings that ended in silence; listened again with the second call, before it finally was answered.

"Sorry", Mark said, "she's still in London."

One of these days, he must call on Mark and Adele – they'd looked after Sophie so well – like a second family she'd said.....When the guests had gone, his family lingered a while. Emboldened by whisky he'd almost relented. Why not tell them? I've met a girl called Sophie – she's everything I could wish for – she's Jewish by the way, very cosmopolitan and her family's still in Berlin. They've lost their home, everything. But they're coming to live here and then you can all meet. And when this war's over, we plan to marry! He'd held back, let the moment pass. Then Edward had sprung that bombshell: *Married! And who is this Frances person, may we ask?* - what chance of a sympathetic hearing after that?

Next morning, all they had were a few moments before Tom's train left.

"What's that behind your back?...From Bon Marche? Tom, how extravagant!"

"It's just a small thing," he'd said quickly, fearful now of its being below expectations. He'd remembered her telling him how she and her mother regularly wore such gloves to all kinds of functions. Now he watched, as expertly, she pulled one on and, with her other hand, fastened its row of tiny pearl buttons. Her movements, light and poised, struck him like those of the Munnerly girls in the painting. Only no layer upon layer of fabric constraints here - this girl was alive and brimming over with excitement.

"You clever thing to guess my size. And now it's my turn."

From within its marbled box, tied with green ribbon, he'd opened up the miniature leather bound volume of psalms. Inside, she had written *O Sing unto the Lord a new song; for He hath done marvellous things. From Sophie Erlich; August 1939*

"Thank you."

In time the Rockies may crumble, Gibraltar may tumble

It didn't of course – tumble. Takes more than love or wars to flatten Gibraltar, but getting there was something else.... the ship rolled like hell across the Bay of Biscay. Tom was sick for two days. With its bay a mass of different fleets and the small town bulging with military, it was clear something big was about to happen. The waiting and training were long and arduous. Nothing though could have prepared him for what followed in Egypt, Italy and Greece.

Somewhere, en route, between Monte Cassino and Perugia, Tom and the depleted 'Kings' took shelter in a deserted palazzo. Amongst its rubble and fragments of sculptures, he'd found the remains of two figures entwined; surely a copy of Bernini's superb Apollo and Daphne? Around its base, an inscription, Bernini's own perhaps? What was it – *Those who pursue fleeting pleasure, Find only leaves and bitter berries?*

Once, he'd have lavished time; used the finest pen and washes of colour, built up their forms, layer by layer. Here, all he had was a pencil stub and an empty cigarette packet.... it would have to do. Edmund would relish the job and Tom knew where, in Havana House, the finished piece would go. What he had to do now was stay alive; then for him and Sophie, the Munnerly's past and the war's brutality could be buried once and for all. It wasn't easy. God knows from the cold, wet exposed terrain of Italy; to the hell in Athens with its house to house fighting, he'd wondered if he would make it back. But he had: first with a sense of shame and then relief as one of fourteen wounded. He'd been fortunate. His wounds, light enough for a brief convalescence and his prompt release from duties had afforded him at last the joy of seeing those familiar birds on Liverpool's waterline and walking those familiar streets; streets and buildings battered as badly as any he'd seen.

They're only made of clay...

"Imagine," Nancy said as she handed Tom the letter. "All these years, it's been sitting, gathering dust in the Philharmonic

Hall. Somebody, a person called Mark I think it was, left it there for you."

The ink looked so fresh…

27th August, 1939

My darling Tom,

Forgive me for not writing sooner. I've been waiting for news from London. As I feared, there is to be no more immigration. Only the most important people will be allowed to stay. Mr Hoechst was kind though. He's arranged for Mama and Papa to travel to Canada and for me to join them there. After the war, we can all return to England.

Isn't it strange Tom, now the war has us both travelling to faraway places? I don't like to think of the distance between us. Everyone says it won't be for long, and then we'll be happy, won't we?

I've booked on the Athenia. She sails this Saturday, which is very sudden, but as Mark says, with school closed and the emergency plans in the city, the sooner the better. And I'm lucky – for already, sailings to Canada are being restricted. Tomorrow, Adele and I are shopping for warmer clothing. The temperature in Montreal right now is fifty seven and getting colder! Tell me, how are things with you? Is it still hot in Gibraltar? It must feel strange now all the inhabitants have left? Though you'll still have the company of those monkeys? You should have a photo taken with one – like the one when you were ten years old. It's still quite the fashion apparently!

I'll leave this with Mark: it's quicker than sending it from the ship. I'll write down everything that happens from the moment we leave Liverpool – we can read it together in our old age!

For now my darling Tom, wish me well. I shall think of you every minute of every day and like our old friend Apollo, play lots of our favourite tunes, until we meet again. You can take care of Venus! May God bless us both.

From your loving
Sophie.

How long, Tom wonders, since he last sat here? *In time, the Rockies may crumble...* 'Here' is Box 18, with its funny sideways view of the orchestra – his father enjoyed that. The years have left their mark though: some of the platform lights don't work and these seats, like the sketch in his pocket, they're frayed at the edges; they've seen better days. Like the couple in the interval, reading their programme. Were they also there that opening evening? Had they once felt the heady delight he'd felt every time he set eyes on Sophie?

He'll never know now how Apollo and Venus might have looked, in pride of place at Havana House. Just as Arthur and Nancy and the rest of the family, knew nothing of Sophie. Those first weeks at home, how Nancy had clung to him, it was as if he'd never been away. And with the news of Edward's death fresh in everyone's minds, it seemed best for him to leave it like that.

He'd nearly told them. When reports of Nuremberg filled every paper and broadcast, it was as if she were alive again and there beside him; waiting for him to do the decent thing. But what would have been the point? She'd gone. All that pain lived over again and for what?

Years later, at breakfast, when Arthur said, "You have to hand it to them, these Jews!" Tom had caught his breath: watched the early morning sun light up the polished table and his mother's silver hair.

"Which ones?" she asked. "There are so many in the papers

just now."

"The ones at Bletchley Park."

He'd shown her the relevant article.

"Seems without them we'd have been hard pressed to break the German codes – no doubt about it, they're clever; they have their uses."

What was it Sophie said on that opening night? Something about a song, a hall and a greeting; a dream, so sweet and fleeting? All too far off now; almost forgotten; like his little book of psalms tucked away in his desk.....

'You knew the Athenia was lost? So, you see, I never married ... Well, Joni, my dear,' I remember Great Uncle Tom saying as the afternoon cast huge shadows across the ghost of the Turkey carpet, 'you did ask.'

Dodger

The Munnerlys kept a variety of pets, dogs in particular. There was even a small pet graveyard in the grounds of Havana House at one time. Pictured here is Dodger, a lurcher that Great Uncle Edward found starving in the docks and brought home. After the war it became Tom Munnerly's dog and lived to a ripe old age. But he always referred to it as 'Edward's dog'.

Dodger's picture was one of the few bits of ornamentation he allowed in his private rooms.

CHAPTER 8

You'll understand in a bit why I'm still putting off Great Aunt Flo. Here's something I picked up on the way: it's about the right place to put it in.

Over the years the Munnerlys have had servants galore. By the time I took an interest, Annie Smith was the only one left.

Annie Smith

From an interview recorded at Park Lodge Care Home, Spital, on June 15 2008

I'd worked for the Munnerly family since time immemorial - you say there's a book being written about them? God knows why. Anyway, nothing to do with me, really. Do I have my own ideas about the family? (Joan, did you say your name was?) Too right, Joan.

I was their housekeeper for years. I worked four days a week and sometimes on a Saturday night if anything special needed cooking. Elsie was the daily who did the rough work, the washing and floors mainly. Coal for the fires. Elsie was a real good sort.

It wasn't much of a wage but I got my meals there.

I lived with Alf, my hubby, down by the Birkenhead docks. He was a fitter at Cammel Laird's. We only had a little two-up, two down but it suited us and we were happy enough. He's dead now so it's different but there you go.

Anyway, I got stuck working for the Munnerlys. They were an interesting lot, I'll say that for them. The brother, Mr Munnerly, you hardly saw him. I liked Miss Margery

Munnerly, although she was a bit bossy at times and wrote poetry. She'd walk round the house in a kind of trance. Sometimes she muttered to herself. I think she was trying to get an idea right- or got stuck with her rhymes, she was educated, you see, which I never was. All because I had a stupid mother and because when I asked a question she never knew the answer, so I got nowhere. I saw to it our daughter, Sonia, went to college. Mind you, she's clever – more like her dad. I didn't want her to get married too soon and get welded to a sink.

Miss Margery had a son, illegit of course, but sort of kept under wraps as the well-off do. I always knew he'd turn out to be shifty. He used to fetch up at odd times, probably short of cash, stay a few days, then take off again. His steady was a conceited, dark little piece. Nobody took to her.

It was a funny house. Georgina, they called her Georgie, Margery's sister, was very nice, quiet but very down in the mouth. She'd been married to a fellow called Jack and lived for years in Liverpool with their twin girls. Jack was killed in the war, so they all came to live with Margery. I got the impression that Jack was dull but decent. Georgie just pottered about. I don't think she had much in common with Margery's way of life – the poetry business.

As for the eldest sister, Florence, very weird she was. She used to weep a lot in her room on the top floor. She said she'd taken a wrong turning. Alf said, 'Take no notice, just do your job.' Georgie and Florence never had meals with Margery when she had people to dinner – other poets they usually were. I couldn't make out what they were talking about but Margery used to perk up with company.

One thing about that house, there was plenty of space. Not light exactly but very airy. I mean you had room to breathe. The furniture was big and comfortable and Georgie was very good on flower arrangements. I do like a bit of colour in a place, don't you? Miss Margery always seemed to like some colour. Often emerald green or petrol blue. Not that she was one for dressing up, as time went on. I think the poetry writing took over.

There was a terrible rumpus one day, I remember I had an appointment with the chiropodist as my feet had been killing me and I wanted to leave early when I heard this big row between Margery and Florence and then an awful crash as though one of them had fallen. I belted upstairs- well as fast as my feet let me - and sure enough, there's Florence, poor thing, was lying on the carpet. Whether she fell or Margery pushed her I don't know. Sisters, eh? Glad I never had any. These two'd been arguing about some letters in a tin box that one of them had found. Some family history stuff – dead as a dodo, I should think. Anyrate, I couldn't wait because of my appointment so I just suggested they should have a cuppa.

Next day there was still a funny atmosphere. Margery was a bit less talkative than usual but I think she was quite tough underneath. I once asked Sonia about her, she said Margery was probably a bit fey. I think money was at the bottom of their troubles - and the shortage of men. They weren't happy – that's a fact.

It was an awful day, that Friday, drizzly, wet and grey. I went to Platt's the fish shop on the way to work – it's gone now, more's the pity. I thought I'd play safe and make fish pie, it being Friday. Margery was having Stephen Somebody-Spencer it might have been, another poet anyhow! - to stay the night, with some woman friend. In the same room. Margery was in a right tiz, going on about the washing and the beds needing making up, not that she did much and Elsie'd had a funny turn and been off for days.

So what with one thing and another I said to Sonia, 'This place is getting me down. I mean, there's Margery and her moods when she's worrying about Peter and his scrapes with girls and Flo's getting quite bronchial – reminds me of Alf's mother, who used to cough a lot like that, as for poor Georgie, well...'

Sonia said, 'Mum, let them get on with it. I'll help you out if you get stuck for cash.'

That settled it. I decided I could manage. I went to the pictures with my new neighbour, Hilda, that night. The thing was, I'd made up my mind. I'd hand in my notice the next day.

And I did. When I told her – Margery, I mean – she turned red in the face, then white. She said, 'Oh no, you mustn't. I've got a seminar here in a fortnight.'

'A what?' I said.

She was really upset, said all these years I'd held the place together. Anyway, the upshot was I said I'd stay on for a bit. I got a rise, which was nice. I felt quite pleased.

I talked to Mac about it. Mac is Mr McNeil, who looks after the garden and comes in three days a week. I gave him his morning tea as usual in the butler's pantry. No one could overhear us there. I liked Mac, very steady, he was and kept things to himself. I said to him, 'You seem to know when things come to an end and I'm at that stage now.'

'Don't worry,' he said. 'Me and the missus will keep in touch and tell you how they're all getting on. I don't suppose things'll change much.'

So come the end of the month I left, I really did. I still saw Mac and Elsie for years after and got the gossip and we had a good laugh about it. So that was fine by me.

It's very nice here. I don't have to do anything.

Feminism and respectability

(Just one last thing and then I'll definitely do Great Aunt Florence.)

It happened in those years leading up to the Second World War. Despite the past work of the

Suffragette movement the balance of power between men and women was still heavily weighted in favour of men. Condemnation for sexual relationships outside marriage or before marriage was the norm but it was the woman who bore the brunt of society's censure. To become pregnant in such circumstances was a stigma for the girl and her family, and it was not unusual to 'cover up' such behaviour by an illegal abortion, adoption or the pretence that the new-born child was a late child of its grandparents. A number of families, even the 'best' would have had aunts/uncles and nieces/nephews growing up as siblings.

This need for secrecy was the greater the more the family aspired to social recognition, and although there may have been exceptions to the rule, certainly in the Munnerly family in the 1930s and 40s the social disgrace brought about by the pregnancy of an unmarried daughter would have been considerable. It was in this moral setting that Florence Munnerly's actions were moulded.

Florence

I made the last entry in my diary today - 21st October 2005. Of course when I was born it would have been The Year of Our Lord 2005. But like so much else that I once thought important, it is the sort of thing belonging to another century.

When I put down my pen I knew it was for the final time, there's nothing else to say, nothing else to be written, it's all in the black leather-bound book, my trusted friend over many years.

Florence Munnerly - her story.

Eighty-seven years - it's a long story, too. Enough to make one of those weighty novels that filled the library shelves of my old home. I remember my mother saying, 'A diary should be a record of all the remarkable things that happen in one's life.' Well, to me they *were* quite remarkable at the time, but now I'm not so sure – remarkable? When I watch some of the programmes on television today.......

There seemed no need to keep a record when I was a young girl. My life was fairly uneventful - happy even. After all I was a Munnerly and that meant something once. I was the middle child of five with two older brothers and two younger sisters. Georgina and I were closest with only one year's difference. "More like twins than sisters," people who saw us together said.... if only we'd known the implications of that remark. But no - in our innocence we shared a bedroom, swapped clothes and exchanged childish secrets. She was lovely, Georgina, in face and disposition. Margery, born when I was eight, was a totally different character. I often wondered what Mother and Father had done to deserve Margery. She wasn't an easy child and became very intemperate- wild even- bohemian in her ways as she got older. I tried to ignore her as much as possible.

We lived in Havana House – how I loved that house! Its gardens had once run down to the River Mersey giving wonderful views across the river to Liverpool, especially from the bedrooms. Even when they were lost, Georgie and I would sit in the window seat and listen to the shipping in the river. We'd make up tales of where they'd been or were going. We longed to be aboard and cross the ocean to lands of adventure. To reach our bedroom off the galleried landing we passed a huge portrait of some of our ancestors, a mother, father and ten children – ten always seemed rather excessive to me – nine of whom were girls. Maybe one of them was a Margery – what a thought! I was fascinated by that painting, though. How stern and proper they all looked.

Perhaps I should have made more effort to research their lives, it's very popular these days. Even Joni, Margery's granddaughter, says she's interested. Came here the other day and tried to push a microphone under my nose and ask me questions about 'the good old days'. I'll give her 'the good old days' – she got short shrift from me. It's the first time she's visited since I moved in a few months ago, not exactly a caring and concerned member of our younger generation. She takes after her father, Peter. Now, if I want a good example of a Munnerly not to be relied on I need look no further, but what else could I have expected from Margery's son?

I'm getting ahead of myself, I must slow down and try and put events in chronological order. It's just if I start writing about Peter there's too much I want to say – none of it good! Ironically I overheard Peter telling someone that his Aunt Flo, despite her acid manner, had a soft spot for him. The only soft spot in that statement was in his head.

Our elder brothers, Tom and Edward, didn't have a great deal to do with us. It must have been a trial to them at times having three sisters, but a definite improvement on nine which is what previous Munnerly sons had had to cope with! And Nancy our mother favoured them. I and Georgina were left to our own devices… which meant that when I met Harold, a clerk at Cammel Lairds Shipbuilders, she was the only one who knew. I often wonder what Harold thought of me, that night at Lecture Hall, lit only by the lantern slides. 'The Glories of Ancient Rome'. I was tall and slim in those days, with long dark hair almost down to my waist – he loved my hair. He was no taller than I and only a year older, and although we were both shy we were relaxed in each other's company. Georgie, despite being younger than me, had already met her husband-to-be, Jack, who had been accepted as <u>suitable</u> by Mother and Father. As Jack's parents and ours met in the same circle of society the courtship progressed quickly, and in the summer of 1939 Georgina and Jack were married on a day so hot it scorched away the storm clouds hanging over Europe. Not for long regrettably. When war broke out both Jack and Harold were called up. Jack was commissioned as a junior officer, but my Harold was a private soldier. I'll never forget the day I saw Harold off on the troop train, straining to catch a last glimpse of him in the sea of khaki spilling from the windows. Even now, many years since the passing of steam, I can still smell it and feel the sense of apprehension and high adventure that evaporated as the train disappeared, leaving only tears and a sense of loss.

Just remembering unblocks the waterways of my eyes. I can still hear Harold's final words to me as if it were yesterday. "I'll be back soon, lass, and then we'll paint the town red."

Well, part of his prediction came true, but Harold painted a field in France instead. And then, as if that wasn't heartache enough, I discovered the predicament he'd left me in.

Georgina – wonderful, dear Georgie – she was my lifeline. She guessed my problem before I even realised it myself. I was stricken by the news of Harold's death, news I'd learnt second-hand. As ours was an unacknowledged courtship, I secretly scoured the newspaper lists, but never thought to find Harold's name so soon. The grief caused by his dying... and the predicament caused by his life... both would soon have become common knowledge without Georgina's help.

Since their wedding Georgina and Jack had moved across the river to Liverpool and a home of their own, a fine three storey villa near the park. As she was expecting, it seemed almost inevitable that she should ask me to move in with her while Jack was at the war. Nothing to arouse suspicion there. Our brothers, Tom and Edward, were both overseas so, leaving mother and father to cope with Margery as best they could, I joined Georgina. Looking back, it amazes me that we managed to keep my condition a secret. A combination of careful dressing and a supposedly delicate constitution helped. As our confinements took place within a convenient ten days of each other the difference in size was negligible, and when mother came across a week after Georgina's daughter, Hazel, was born she had no suspicion that Hazel's 'twin', Caroline, was a granddaughter from a different source. A brace of Munnerly babies, bonny and dark-haired beneath their identical bonnets, gave no cause for anxiety. Her delight at the twins' arrival was apparent to any neighbours who called in.

'It's so clever of Georgina to have twins – of course they run in the family you know.' If her strong face clouded at the memory of a past loss, she soon rattled on with, 'Oh yes, Georgina has done us proud. We're so thrilled that twins have appeared again – clever Georgina.'

But one comment wounded me more than any other.

'It's a pity you haven't found a nice young man, Flo! Just think, you could be married now and nursing your own little angel.'

I wanted to scream into her face, 'I found a wonderful young man and we have a beautiful baby, but he's dead. I'll never see him again and he'll never know or see his beautiful daughter.' Instead I gritted my teeth, smiled until my face ached and murmured something unintelligible. Despite the dangers that war brought I loved the time we spent together, just the four of us, except when Jack was home on leave. I pleaded with Georgina not to tell him the truth. I wept and begged until – fearing, I think, for my sanity - she acquiesced. I so wanted my Caroline to have a father and a legitimate birth certificate that no whiff of scandal could touch.

Jack's leaves became rarer as the war progressed, and I would have happily stayed on the Liverpool side of the river, but the bombing raids by the Luftwaffe drove us back to Havana House at the beginning of May 1941. It turned out to be a life-saving decision when the May blitz rained terror on everyone living in the city, and our happy home in the Kirkdale district became just one of the many craters transforming the landscape. The resilience of Liverpudlians during that fearful time was legendary, but I for one was relieved to be removed from the centre of the mayhem, especially as my chief concern in life – no, my only concern- was the safety of Caroline. I watched the city across the river burn night after night, my child pressed safely to me in the dark where no one could see my face.

Georgina's plans to return after the war were changed dramatically. Not simply by the destruction of the house – houses can rise again, houses can be purchased - but by her husband's death during the D-Day landings. If I'm honest, I'll admit that my attempts to comfort Georgina in her bereavement were mixed with a feeling of relief that I would not be separated from Caroline when the war ended. Edward's loss at sea late in the war had been difficult time for us all, especially Mother and Father. The suggestion that Georgina, I and the girls should make Havana House our permanent home was one they were only too happy to make and we to accept.

After the decision was made Georgina tried for one last time to persuade me to tell the truth about Harold- and about Caroline. 'Flo, it may be difficult at first, but just think how much easier it will be in the long run. Tell everyone the truth! Caroline means so much to you, it must be agony not being able to admit she's yours. It would be a shock to people, but so many things are happening at the moment! This would be a nine days wonder and then forgotten. Mother and Father are so upset about Edward and - well, Tom is so quiet since he came back, they'd soon get over it.'

But I could not. It wasn't so much the thought of Mother, Father and Tom knowing (I couldn't care less about Margery), it was the thought of Carrie herself. The thought of her hating me when she was old enough to know she was illegitimate was more than I could bear. So I ignored Georgina's advice and went on playing the role of a doting Aunt Flo.

Our younger sister, Margery, started at Girton in the post-war years – Margery was always something of a bluestocking, an unconventional person, and I wasn't sorry her influence would be removed from my Caroline – the timing worked well. Edward's death during the war had hit our parents hard, especially Father, and although Tom's return had been of some comfort, the continued presence of two daughters – one errant, if they'd but realised – and two granddaughters, was a welcome distraction. I'd been fonder of Tom, and although sad about Edward we had never been close. As the oldest of the five Munnerly children Tom had always been protective of his younger brother and sisters although, quite frankly, at times I felt that he needed protecting from Margery. Something had been broken inside Tom that he could never tell us about. Nor could it be healed - certainly he was never to marry nor carry on with the business. That would be left to others, to paid employees, from this time on. It was as though he had come to hate the sea and all things connected with it. I, however, soon picked up the threads of family living but what I hadn't realised was how irked I would feel at being unable to claim the delightful, growing girl as my own. On reflection, I wonder whether it really would have mattered so much if the truth… but at the time it had seemed imperative. In fact the most important thing I could do for my child. A respectable name was vital.

Writing that last sentence has made me think of Margery. A good reputation hadn't been high on her list of attainments when she'd finally arrived home in 1955 after travelling goodness knows where and doing goodness knows what after graduating - with an admittedly respectable degree. I saw her the very day she came back from America, though she never knew I did. The memory of her casually strolling up the drive, wearing trousers if you please. A crimson scarf was knotted about her throat and her eyebrows plucked to pencil lines…and with a babe in her arms!

It's cruelly vivid. It still makes my blood pressure rise. The brashness of the girl! Simply to come home as if she'd been shopping that afternoon and bought a baby in the children's department at Beatties. The brazenness was overwhelming. No proper explanation, no contrition, just some tom-fool story about the father no longer being necessary. Well, Caroline's father had been necessary, very necessary to me, but I'd been forced to manage without him, and without bringing disgrace on our name.

The most galling thing about Margery's reappearance was that it didn't bring any disgrace on her. Unusual as a child, her bohemian way of living became almost a source of family pride.

'Oh, Margery never was one for convention,' I heard Mother telling one of her friends, 'and Peter is such a dear. And a boy - that's important as it ever was. The two girls are lovely of course, but we're so thrilled to have a grandson.'

Whether it was the ill-concealed preference of his grandmother for Peter that coloured my view, or the circumstance of his birth, I continued to feel little affection for him… unlike Georgina who was only too happy to pick up the maternal mantle that Margery passed on with the regularity of an Olympic torch bearer.

So our lives continued at Havana House. After Mother and Father died Tom, Georgina and I became the older generation and lived peacefully together. Margery like a bad penny had already returned - with her bad half-penny in arms. We were down to life in a very few rooms with very little help, just a couple to do the heavy work and a woman to cook for us, still. Aggy, I think her name was, or Annie- always lurking.

Having Caroline as my daughter, even unacknowledged, has been the highlight of my life. As an indulgent 'aunt' I was able to keep close to both girls and, although I tried not to, I fear I favoured my own. Her dark, glossy hair, clear skin and large trusting eyes, reminding me of Harold's, were far more appealing than Hazel's mousy appearance. My darling girl far out-shone in handsomeness any of that gaggle of Munnerly ancestors in the great portrait. Georgina sometimes gently reprimanded me, but as the only other person who knew the truth she understood my motives, and Carrie – so I believe – has the sweeter personality.

It was six years ago I first noticed poor Georgina becoming confused. Margery was dead, of a sudden, of course, and now my sister's fragile mind did not survive the turn of the century. We'd both become rather forgetful, not unusual at our age, and we would often amuse ourselves by seeing who was worst. However, it was one thing to walk into a room and wonder why you were there; it was quite another not to recognise the room. Initially I was able to smooth things, but it soon became apparent to other members of the family that Georgina's problems were just beginning. Offensive phrases like 'senile dementia' were bandied about. Why does everything need an official medical term? When I was a young girl most families had a grandparent or aged aunt who was a little 'odd in the head', but they were just accepted as part of the family. Nowadays it seems the main aim of many of the younger generation is to dispose of their elders by dispatching them to residential homes and then make the occasional, and well-heralded, guilt-freeing visit

I was sure my Carrie wouldn't countenance such a thing, but then I was horrified to overhear her talking to Hazel, 'Mum's forgetfulness really is becoming a problem. I'm worried she'll hurt herself when we're not here.' They had both by this time flown the nest and the joy of their joint visits was suddenly poisoned for me.

'I know,' Hazel said, "I suppose it'd be possible for her to take turns living with us. We can't expect Aunt Flo or Uncle Tom to look after her all the time – not at their age.'

Their age indeed – what cheek!

'We may be able to manage Mum between us,' Hazel went

on, 'and that won't be easy, but there's no way I could cope with Aunt Flo or Uncle Tom if either of them went the same way – they'd have to go into a nursing home.'

'But Aunt Flo's always been so good to us. Almost a second mother.'

'Well we don't need to think about that yet,' Hazel said, 'she's still got most of her marbles.'

There'd been a lump in my throat at what Caroline said but Hazel's comment nearly choked me. It just goes to prove what I've always said about Carrie having the sweeter nature.

Now I thought back to the incident with Tom. We were discussing the girls and for some reason the subject of their names was raised. Tom was querying the choice of Hazel and Caroline for the twins, Caroline being our grandmother's name but Hazel a very unusual one for a Munnerly. Before I could say anything Georgina burst in.

'Oh, I've always liked the name Hazel, but you know Flo, she's fanatical about the family, it had to be a family name for Caroline.'

For a moment my mind went blank as I realised the implications of that remark. I had to say something – and quickly. 'Georgina was so kind to me when she knew she was having twins and… and, as Jack was away at that time, she let me have a say in choosing one of the names.' I'd laughed nervously, 'I expect that's why I've always had such a soft spot for darling Carrie.'

Tom seemed to accept this but he looked puzzled by Georgina's sudden, and repeated, apology.

'I'm so sorry Flo, so sorry. It just slipped out – I didn't think.'

And that was the problem – she didn't think properly. Her powers of rational thought were diminishing, and the dangerous comments were becoming more frequent. I felt as if my secret was hanging over me like Damocles' sword, the thread fraying like the edges of Georgina's mind. What could be done? I'd kept my secret for so long – it was my life, I couldn't bear the thought of it becoming common knowledge.

The diabetes that Georgina had developed in middle age gave me the perfect opportunity. Her need to self-inject had become a matter of some concern within the family, especially as she became more confused, and it had been arranged for the district nurses to administer her insulin- or me on occasion.

The awfulness of that day has never left me. I've tried to put it from my mind, to tell myself it was for the best, that Georgina only had years of misery ahead of her, but I was wrong – the misery has been mine. I held her hand as she slipped into her final coma – <u>she even thanked me</u>. 'You're so good to me, Flo. I don't know what I'd do without you.'

So the secret is mine alone. No-one to talk to, no-one to exchange a glance with if Caroline is mentioned, no-one with whom I can be proud of what my daughter has become. I not only lost a sister, I lost my other self. At times I felt I might have lost my reason, too. Even my love for Carrie – the love that has consumed my whole life – seemed diminished by the death of Georgina. This, then, is my punishment – to be without her. No prison sentence would seem so bleak, no justice more fitting.

At times, even now, that day remains clear as glass. I can still smell the hyacinths in a planter on the coffee table, feel the cold smoothness of the leather settee where we sat together holding hands as hers cooled in my grasp, sense the clamminess of my other hand gripped tightly around the syringe in my pocket. I can see the sorrow on Tom's face when I called for help – I think it was what killed him within the year. I can hear the devastation in my darling Carrie's voice when I telephoned. Over and over again she kept saying, 'Not Mummy, oh no, no, no.'

Well, it wasn't – <u>I was her mother</u> – but I couldn't say that. And my lips are still sealed – on both my secrets.

As the years go on, the girls remember Georgina with love

and affection, but the grief has lessened. Perhaps that, too, has been transferred – I feel so weary.

Today Peter called at Havana House, a very rare occurrence – did I say, true to form, he'd left it under a cloud? He came straight to my room, an even rarer one. Having eyed up the Gillows chest and console table (both original to the house) without further preamble he launched into what was obviously a prepared speech. 'Great Aunt Flo, maybe it's time you should consider living somewhere with a bit more support.'

The measured tones, so unlike his normal slapdash speech, made the phrase, 'young whippersnapper' hover on my lips but, unusually for me when dealing with Peter, I held back from speaking my mind. It didn't stop me thinking it.

'After all,' he went on, 'you've had one or two falls recently. I mean I'm - well, the family, are concerned. It's not as if good old Annie was still with you. Rattling around in this big old place…'

Not for the first time it occurred to me that the amount of concern Peter had shown for anyone in his life was minimal. There must be some hidden purpose behind his visit. When he was a young boy I'd heard him to refer to Georgina and myself as 'a plague of aunts!' Well, I was quite happy to continue to plague him, but I wished that Georgina was still here to assist. How I missed Georgina – could it really be six years since she'd passed away? That's the phrase I use.

'So I'll leave you to have a think about it. Eh?'

As he got up to go the knowledge that I had hardly listened to a word gave me considerable satisfaction. Ever since the first sight of my new nephew as a mewling infant I'd found it difficult to feel any affection for him or - in the jargon of day-time television, a lingo I despise myself for using – to bond. His arrival had brought on emotions not normally associated with a young baby, and nothing he had done since had changed them.

The day after Peter's visit Carrie arrived, looking serious.

I'd hoped to joke with her about Peter's suggestion that I couldn't cope without help, but what she herself had come to tell me was much, much worse… a knife to my heart.

'Darling Aunt Flo, I've got this old school friend, Margaret Wayne - you remember little Maggy don't you? Well, she's in Australia now - has been for a couple of years. Just like me - not married. She's asked me to go and stay with her. It's something I'm considering. Well, I've made up my mind, really. Ever since Mum died I've felt - restless. I know it's a long way, but Hazel and Ian and their girls are close by, you'll see plenty of them. Well not the girls, perhaps, but - and of course I'll write regularly and send lots of photographs. But - but now, you see I'm past retirement age - even for a lawyer! I may stay there, especially if it's as good as she claims. Maybe you'll be able to come out and visit me…'

As she said this last sentence her voice faltered as she must have seen the anguish flood into my expression. Over the years I'd tried so hard to keep my self-control, to be firm but fair, at times affectionate but always restrained. Now all that was slipping away, and with horror I felt the tears fill my eyes and trickle down my cheeks. I felt my lip, which had begun to tremble as Caroline spoke, twist into an ugly line

'Don't go, please don't go – you can't leave me.'

The whisper came out as a croak.

Concern on Carrie's face at my reaction now turned to acute embarrassment. 'But Aunt Flo, it's only a trial – I may hate it there, and it's only twenty-four hours away – I'll be back to visit. I know how you miss Mum yourself. I mean, it'd be different if she was still alive, but as it is…' She smiled faintly, a smile of both puzzlement and exasperation.

Next week will be the first anniversary of Caroline's departure for Perth.

Needless to say, she loves it there and, although planning a return visit next year, has made it clear in her letters that she intends to stay.

192 Mimosa Lane
Beechboro Cove
Perth
Christmas Eve, 2004

Darling Aunt Flo,

How are you? I think of you often and hope that you're comfortable in your nice new home, and not at all unsettled. I wish you were able to come to me for a holiday. I would love to take you up to King's Park and show you the city that has quite stolen my heart. Perth is such a lovely place and the people I've met here have been so kind and welcoming. My experiment to rent has been a great success so much so I've decided to apply for residency and maybe buy my own small place when and if that is granted. I shall miss you (I still miss dear Uncle Tom!) and of course Hazel and her family, but I feel so happy here – as if a whole new life is opening up for me. As you know I'm planning to visit you just after Christmas – I'll be able to tell you if turkey tastes different when the temperature is 30 degrees outside!

You'll never guess what...

So it went on, excitement spilling from every line of her dear, familiar scrawling hand. It left me in no doubt that her future was settled. Mine is too. How ironic that Peter's suggestion has become prophetic. I felt I could have continued at Havana House unaided, but he and Hazel thought differently – even Joni with her wires and microphones wasn't much support. I told them the thought of falling didn't worry me, I'd take my chances. But they were pressing- and in the end I didn't have the energy to argue.

Here I am in my room with the flowered curtains that do not match the flowered bedspread, nor the flowered carpet. Surrounded by flowers in my nice new home- and waiting to be put to bed. That's my life now – waiting.

……waiting for dinner
……waiting for the toilet (especially that)
……waiting for bed
……**not** waiting for bingo or quizzes
……waiting for the nurse with the fat bottom to go off duty
……waiting for Carrie

She'll be here soon, I know she will. I've told the nurse over and over again.

'My daughter will be coming soon – any day now - she'll get me out of here.'

They assume we're all deaf. Do you know what I heard her say as she left the room? 'That old biddy in Number 24 – tells everyone she's got a daughter who's going to come and take her home. Sad really. She's just an old spinster – rude too.'

Well she has got a fat bottom!

Dear Aunt Flo,

Unlike Carrie, I don't ever remember writing to you in my life or yours. In death, you've left me with nothing to say.

Joni

Georgina Munnerly on her wedding day. Her dress of cream figured satin was made by Sloan's of 42,Bold Street, Liverpool.

CHAPTER 9

Well, Great Aunt Flo, I thought I'd try to explain, to put a better gloss on things but- no there's still not a thing I can add.

Here's my grandmother - or at least here are the bits of evidence.

Margery

Document 1

St Teresa's Girls' High School,
Bickenstead Road,
Oxton,
Wirral,
Cheshire.

18th August, 1943

Dear Mr Munnerly,

I am writing further to our recent conversation. May I express my thanks to you for sparing the time to call and discuss the matter in hand?

Following the lines of our agreement during your visit I have recommended to the Board of Governors that the School should adopt a lenient attitude towards Margery's behaviour at the end of term. This would not normally have been the School's policy; several years ago a girl was asked to leave for engaging in a lesser escapade. The placing of potassium permanganate in the School's water supply, in particular, drew strong demands for her expulsion from a number of parents who felt, despite my reassurances, that their daughters might have been permanently damaged by the prank. It was the publicity which this outcry attracted which unfortunately brought the matter to the attention of the Governors and indeed the wider public.

However, in view of Margery's undoubted ability and our reluctance to waste her talents, I have submitted a request that she should merely be punished by a series of detentions and a severe warning and happily the Board has acceded.

There is, however, one further matter. Margery drew deserved praise for her portrayal of Cleopatra in the School's summer production of Shakespeare's play but a number of parents have complained that her display of bosom went beyond what was necessary for the application of the asp and was not in keeping with the School's tradition and standards. I would be grateful if, bearing in mind the confidential nature of these comments on a sensitive matter, you would kindly pass them on to Margery in reinforcement of what I have already said to her, and see that behaviour of this kind is never repeated.

Thank you again for visiting St Teresa's. I hope that this will draw a veil over our recent tribulations.

Yours sincerely,

Edith Meade, B. A. (Edinburgh)

Headmistress

Document 2

St Teresa's Girls' High School

Term Report: Winter 1943

Name: Margery Rosina Munnerly

Age: 15 years 3 months

Form: 5A

Art: Margery shows promise and even a certain artistic flair but must learn greater perseverance and attention to detail.

French: Has a gift for mimicry which stands her in good stead in French conversation but is weak on grammar.

History: It is important for Margery to learn that imaginative writing is no substitute for a knowledge of the facts.

Geography: Has gained good marks on the Caribbean and the Himalayan Kingdoms but appeared to lose interest when the class turned to the United Kingdom.

Physical Education: Played well for the school's second eleven. Higher things next year?

English: Margery shows a real appreciation of the Romantic poets and the Elizabethan period. Her prose, however, tends to be excessively flowery and verbose. She should try to cultivate a clear, precise style.

Conduct: When interested in the subject, Margery behaves well. She should not, however, allow a certain perversity in her character, or perhaps a dislike of some of her colleagues and teachers, to lure her into acts of mutiny.

Form Mistress's Comments: Margery's record is rather patchy. She should learn to behave with greater decorum and not allow her language and mode of dress to be inappropriately influenced by popular magazines and films.

Document 3

St Teresa's Girls' High School,
Bickenstead Road,
Oxton,
Wirral,
Cheshire.

15th September, 1945

Dear Mr Munnerly,

Thank you for your recent visit.

The School appreciates that you are naturally anxious for Margery to take the entrance examinations for Cambridge, especially in view of the aptitude she has shown in some areas of her academic work. You will, I hope, in turn understand that it would be impossible for the School to recommend her for University entrance if at the same time her conduct obliged us to suspend her from her studies here.

Fortunately, at a meeting I held yesterday with her form mistress and house mistress I succeeded in persuading my colleagues that , despite our considerable distress at her recent conduct, suspension would be too severe a penalty and that the School should therefore be willing to allow her to complete this academic year and with it her school career. I shall be grateful if you will kindly convey this decision to Margery while at the same time impressing upon her the full extent of the concession being made and urge her to act with restraint in all matters during the coming months.

I trust that this outcome will prove satisfactory to you.

Yours sincerely,

Edith Meade B.A. (Edinbrugh)

Headmistress

The letter, like its predecessor is handwritten. I notice Miss Meade, after two more years of Margery's company, can no longer spell the name of her old university.

Not to worry. It's 1955 now. Carl Perkins has just written 'Blue Suede Shoes.' Rock and roll hasn't quite made it to Havana House yet, but it's on its way. Oh yes, baby, it's on its way.

'Hello. Is that you Pops?'

'Arthur Munnerly, yes. Hold on, is that -?

'Yes, it's me, Margery.'

'What a surprise!'

'Listen- is Mother out?'

'Yes.'

'Good. Look, Pops, I'm coming home next week. Flying to Heathrow and then train to Lime Street.'

'We've all been wondering where you've been - for this long a time.'

'You got my postcards?'

'Well, yes. Not that we thought them all very suitable.'

‘I’m ringing because- look, when I arrive, I’m bringing someone else.’

‘You don’t mean you’ve got engaged?’

‘No, not that and not likely to be. I’ve become a mother. Of a son. He’s very healthy – good lungs, at least. Not so good at controlling his other physical motions. I’ll explain when I see you. I just wanted you to know so that at least one person won’t be shocked. You’re still there?’

‘Yes. Yes.’

‘Are you all right?’

‘No.’

‘I should get home on Friday. It’d be nice if my room was ready for me.’

‘It’ll be seen to. Margery -’

‘Lots of love to you. Don’t tell anyone I rang, will you? It’d only give them time to stoke up their prejudices.’

‘Oh, Margery, that’s unkind.’

‘Must go. See you next week.’

‘Yes, darling. And love from us all -.’

But Margery was gone.

Normally she’d have made a scene of it: The Return of the Native. Scenes were her thing. But to knock on the door of Havana House, babe in arms, and have to explain everything seemed too demeaning, too Orphan Annie. They could find out gradually. Still by some miracle she was still in possession of her key to the front door. Margery slid it into the lock and inched in.

No one. Nancy and Arthur would be at church this time on a Sunday morning. Flo and Georgina as well, possibly. Or Georgina might be gardening at the back of the house. Good. Then they could discover her, not she make herself known to them. On tiptoe, she stole down the hall to her room.

Or what should be her room. What would still be her room if they hadn’t got up to any funny business, like turning it into a junk room or handing it over like an ex-army billet to squatters or renting it out to refugees from East Germany or letting Hazel and Caroline run riot in it. For a moment she turned back to survey the hall. Nothing had changed. The gloomy pictures still lined the walls, the lighter-coloured patch remained where The Portrait had once hung. Overbearing, like the rest of this family mausoleum. This hall, the heavy banisters, the creepy gallery itself, God knows – they must have distorted her psyche or ego being brought up in a cavern of a place. She sighed, then grasped the horrid black handle and crept inside.

Unused to the austerity ration of light let in through a window shadowed by cypresses and by the swathes of velvet inside, she flicked the switch. So this was home. Well…

With a squelch she set the baby down on the floor. Peter, she'd decided to call him, she wasn't sure why. She breathed satisfaction at not waking him. Sleepy little thing, wasn't he? More a Munnerly than a Wild West boy.

She looked round for something to wipe wet hands on: nappies had been scarce on the journey back. Ah, this would do - an old sun-dress of the sort Florence used to wear on the beach at Thurstaston. She wouldn't be doing that any more, not an old thing like Florence. It would make an ideal towel. She picked it up, scattering sand on to the fluff-coated carpet that Peter was now starting to taste, and reduced her hands to a faint, keen ammonia smell by vigorous rubbing. She walked to the window and seized the curtain. At a second tug one of the hooks gave way and the velvet sagged, adopting a pose of obesity or possibly pregnancy at one end. Ho ho, here we go. Back to nothing working.

But her case! It must still be standing unguarded at the front door, stuffed with priceless mementoes of travel and romance, all nestling among the dirty underclothes. She started towards the hallway.

But the doorway was already darkening. Slowly, a figure appeared.

'*Margery*!'

'Good God! Flo!'

For a second they stood open-armed, on the brink of joining but held back by an unseen membrane: the older sister made shrunken and pale by years of internment in the gloomy house, the younger with face coppered by sunshine. Then recognition snapped and with the strangeness of new lovers they embraced.

'You didn't write. We thought you might have been in an accident. Even- dead.'

'Me? No, I'm not dead. Not a little bit.' Margery held up arms and hands in proof. 'Hey, I just remembered. My case is still outside.'

'No, I brought it in. I recognised it as one of ours - maybe one of Mother's, I guessed. Here.' She walked back to the passageway and with the grunt of a navvy lifting some heavy gear, lugged the case into the room.

'Heavens! It's full of iron ore!'

But as her load thumped the floor another intrusion caught her eye. She stopped short, incredulous, then approached the weird bundle lying at mid-floor.

'What is it?' Gingerly, with a toe, she prodded the grubby shawl. 'What – on earth – is it?'

'Ah!' Margery sprang to life. In a moment she stood beside Flo, inserting a foot between her sister's shoe and the baby. 'He's all right. He's mine. Peter. I've called him Peter.'

'You've…called…him?'

'Yes. It's his name.' Margery stooped and picked the bundle up. 'Well, he has to be called something. I suppose.'

'But… But where did you…get him?'

'Well, where else but..?' Margery patted her stomach. 'The usual way.' She waved a hand. It was all rather absurd, explaining the obvious.

'But…his father? Who's…his father?'

'Ah. Yes.' What could she say? *Well, I'm not sure, actually. According to some accounts, well, his account really, he's called Lincoln - but according to others, it's H. J. Roover*? No, it wouldn't do. Too long-winded and unfinal. And anyway, she wasn't sure she liked either name. In bed she'd stuck to 'darling' and, once only before rejecting it, 'sweetie-pie'. She could invent a name, of course… Hank was a good one: mentally she resolved to think of him as Hank.

'He was a gift from the gods.' She raised her palms and face heavenward. 'Like Pallas Athene rising from the sea. Or did she spring from Zeus's head? I'm not sure. Probably authorities differ.'

But Flo was serious. 'Margery, don't joke. He is your baby?' She moved aside a curtain of shawl to study the baby's head, crowned by a mat of hair but otherwise spherical as a grapefruit. It looked just like any other baby – a cross between a cherub and Mussolini. Her face broke, close to tears.

'Of course! I don't pick up strays.'

'There's a need for that, too.'

For once a glimpse of her sister's feelings impinged on Margery: as if, for Flo, a foundling would have been a godsend. 'Sorry, yes. No. He's mine. All of him.'

'And he's called Peter…?'

'Um - Munnerly of course.'

'And you're not going to say how…or who?'

It was a perfect let-out. Margery performed three small dance-steps 'No,' she said, 'I'm not.'

Over the years Peter, my father, would hear several versions of this story. Who's to know which if any of them is true?

Margery Munnerly was a noted minor poet in her day so there's nothing I can add to the picture of herself that comes across in her work. Read her. I find her poems a bit self-absorbed, a bit too Margery Munnerly, for my taste. And that's when I can understand them.

Document 4

It is with regret that Poetry Now! announces the death of Margery Munnerly. (1931-1990). During her career she published five slim volumes, the most critically acclaimed being The Sailor's Daughter, (Pan's Press, 1968). Much of her work is no longer available but the poem that first brought her to the public's attention in 1960, Boy in Tears, is still much anthologised.

She is survived by her son, Peter Munnerly, author of the 'Burlington' series of historical adventures.

Margery's most successful book and a rare collector's item.

CHAPTER 10

This is not the way most people find out about their parents' courtship. This is fiction, a piece of fiction written by my father and published in a long-defunct magazine. With the names changed. All I've had to do is reinstate them.

Did he keep a copy? Of course he did!

Peter

When the girl reached the end of the bicycle sheds Peter stepped out. For a moment they stood breathless, sizing each other up.

'You're Peter Munnerly, aren't you? My Mum knows yours.'

He decided to play it cool. 'I know. You're Penny Green' He twiddled his school pen as if it were a cigarette.

'Your Mum's called Margery.'

The subject seemed exhausted. He jammed his pen back into his breast pocket and pointed to his school bag.

'Do you read *Eagle*? If you do I've got some.'

'Old ones?'

'Not that old.' He fished one out. 'What's today's date?'

'Don't know. What's it say?'

'Fifteenth of March.' It didn't seem to help. 'They're sixpence.'

'Where do you get 'em from?'

He raised his head, narrowed his eyes: *Don't get too snoopy.* 'Want to buy one?'

Penny Green wrinkled her nose. Even in a show of disgust there was something fascinating about it, pert and upturned. Peter felt his breath quicken.

'I can get girls' stuff as well.'

'What like?'

'*Girls' Crystal. Miranda* .They're a bit old but you could have them cheap. Five for two bob.'

'Do you make pots of money that way?'

'More'n you think.' Giving nothing away.

He wondered how much she would think. Girls didn't understand about money, only what they could spend it on – clothes and make-up and things like that. They didn't read good stories where you could *become* Dan Dare or Dr Who. He bet she didn't even know what it was like, living Dan Dare's life half the time. And the other half Superman. Girls were stupid.. All the same, when you looked at her…

She gathered herself as if to go and in haste he put a hand on her forearm. Sleeve rolled up for deskwork on a summer day, her flesh was fresh and delicate, starkly contrasting with the orange nicotine stain and the dark hairs of incipient adolescence on his own.

'You ever been in Wardle's shed?'

'Wardle?'

'The groundsman. He used to play goalie for Rovers.'

'He's with your school. Posho! Just 'cos ours is next door doesn't mean -'

'You want to see it. It's great. Just down the path there, the cinder one.'

She seemed reluctant. He sensed the need for charm and smiled, at the same time tightening his grip on her arm. 'It's easy to get in. The lock's broke.'

'Why do you want me to go in there?'

But even while asking she half-understood. She hesitated, expressionless. Shock? Or the bubble of excitement?

'Come on.. No one'll know.' He reached in his pocket and took out a handful of sales money. 'Here, you can have a shilling.'

Her eyes gleamed. He felt the thrill of discovering a like mind. He'd waylaid her for her looks, the long dark locks curtaining her eyes, the enticing way she walked. And the stories about what she'd let you do. But this was something more. The romance of shared capitalism.

She pawed the ground with her foot, undecided. When she spoke her answer was a challenge. 'Half a crown.'

She didn't even check the coin as their feet crunched on cinders.

Here's another . According to a pencilled scribble at the bottom of the page he got £5 for this one - from something called The Inkslinger.

'Your Grandfather wants to see you.'

Uncharacteristically, Margery turned away as she made the announcement. Usually she had a smile (albeit a sarcastic one) on her lips when she spoke to him; today she seemed almost severe.

'What about?'

'He'll tell you.'

By habit Peter searched his mind for things he might have done wrong. Especially at work. Ever since Arthur had got him the job he'd had two bosses to keep sweet: Scrimgeour and his Grandfather. But, perplexingly, there seemed no reason for trouble to have arisen - not yet at any rate. Surely no one can have found out about that nice little scheme he and Red Thomas had going? It was such early days.

'Can't you give me a clue?'

Margery hesitated. Through the silent telegraph linking mother and son he got the message it wasn't to do with work. What then? *Sex?* Oh God. How could that come into it this time? He couldn't imagine. But that would account for the look of indecision on her face: the wanting to reprimand him but not feeling well placed to do it; the hint of a laugh scowled to silence by the Munnerlys' sense of propriety. No one at Havana House ever mentioned sex.

'He'll tell you. You'd better have a good story ready. Go on. He's waiting.'

A sense of heaviness clodhopped with him along the landing. There came to mind the walk to Purlock's study at school, the interview with Scrimgeour at Atlantic Finance. They did it to elevate themselves; they summoned you to make themselves feel important. That was what they wanted most of all, more than money, more than sex, these people who never told you anything, never talked about the things that mattered or that motivated them most. If they'd been his sole source of information he'd never have found out about that shady ancestor and his misdeeds. He wouldn't know how the Munnerlys made their money from the shipfuls of foetid human flesh plying between the Gold Coast and Barbados. He'd certainly never have found out how babies were born. It had been up to Red Thomas and the lads at school – the very people the Munnerlys despised; 'gutter urchins' he'd heard Nancy call them - to tell him anything that mattered in this life.

In a way he quite liked old Arthur. But he was one of them. So caution was vital. Never trust anyone.

He knocked and waited. In the house that was your own home you had to knock, then wait. Always you waited. And why? Not because they were busy: Arthur and Nancy were never busy. Because it made you feel small.

The door opened and Arthur stood there.

'You wanted to see me?'

'Yes.' He gestured Peter in. Another gesture of the head directed him to a chair. Peter stood, pretending not to see, looking round the room. 'You'd better sit down.'

It came to him that his grandfather wasn't acting freely. His Grandmother was nowhere to be seen. (Why not? If this was about trouble at work she would be. She liked nothing better than to play the police inspector, to interrogate). But Arthur, unmistakably, was obeying her orders. Pity grazed Peter's heart. This old, grey man had made the money that kept Nancy silken-dressed in her drawing room. He'd exempted her from employment and housework alike, lifelong. Yet he'd spent a life as her slave. (Now that's an unfortunate word!) Poor fool anyway.

Arthur took an armchair, half-facing him but at an angle. How they feared eye-contact. As the guilty always did. He was fingering a paper.

'I've received this letter.'

Peter reached out and took it. It was written on green, lined paper in a rounded, female-looking hand.

Dear Mr Arthur Munnerly,

I am writing as Penny's mother to tell you something you may not know. Penny has been friendly with your grandson Peter for a long time now, they were at school together and I am sorry to say that she is pregnant. There is no doubt who the father is. It is your Peter and I think we need to make arrangements for them to get married as soon as possible. Please would you get in touch with me at the above address to arrange things?

Yours
Emily Green

'Well. What have you got to say?'

There was no point in denial. 'Do we have to get married? Doesn't seem a good idea to me.'

'Your Grandmother insists on it. This family is- and then your mother is a... a... *an* eminent poet in her own right...'

So much for free love. His guess was right. 'That settles it, does it?'

'Yes, it does.'

'What sort of wedding does Grandmother want?'

'A proper one, of course.'

Peter found he was trembling. 'You mean white?'

'If it can be made to seem appropriate.'

Peter had heard it all before. Nancy, calculating as a blackjack player, discussing other girls' weddings, noting every detail, checking every convention: where the bridegroom stayed the night before the wedding, who were chosen as bridesmaids, if there was to be any promise to obey; whether the bride wore white. For Nancy every symbol had meaning. Truth didn't count.

He expelled breath and surrendered. He wondered to whom this yielding brought the more relief, himself or his grandfather. 'Okay, I'll go and see her, Mrs Green. Only' – he couldn't let it pass – 'why couldn't Penny tell me herself?'

'Hello. I'm Peter. Can I come in?'

With obvious hostility the woman - it must be Mrs Green – let him in. The end-terrace at Canal Street contrasted starkly with Havana House. Its front door opened directly on to the street, its frontage barely four yards wide. In the parlour, where he was ushered, lace curtains shut out the prying eyes of passers-by. Even on a sunny day they cast shadow over the worn, heavy sofa and armchairs, the empty, black-polished grate and, at its side, the potted cheese-plant standing sentinel. An upright piano, also polished under an overload of ornaments and photographs, gave the impression of never being played. Too cramped for any social activity, too dark for sewing or reading, the room's atmosphere was museum-like.

'Well, it's you that did it. What are you going to do?'

For once he stood wordless. At Havana House it had never seemed that there was any choice what he should do. His grandfather had decreed marriage. But here he felt there might be alternatives, space for negotiation.

'You ought to make it right by her. By Penny.'

It was not in Peter's nature to take orders. He took a breath, preparing to argue. But something about the little woman's sad pride held him in check. A woman struggling to keep her house decent against all odds, gloomy and cramped as it was in its wasteland across the street from the canal's rubbish-tipped water. Fighting a losing war. Was that why Penny had never asked him round or introduced him, ashamed of her home and sole surviving parent? Or was there some deeper, bitterer hostility between them?

'I ought to talk to her about it.'

'She's out.' The words were half-swallowed. 'You ought to do the right thing. It's yours. The baby.'

'I know.'

'Well, you're a lad, aren't you?'

Against a fiercer accuser he would have fought back, defended himself. But this lonely, sad figure with her low, grief-stricken voice, her half-crouching posture and the waves of grey yet still comely hair - she'd been pretty once - brought him shame for adding to her troubles. They cast Penny in a new light, too. The girl's perky manner and jokiness, seen from this house, took on a feverishness, a desperate attempt to escape life in Canal Street, the covering-up of a home which, once exposed, might destroy her one means of escape.

'What does Penny want? Does she want us to get married?' Hope surged. Just a hint of it, at least. He hadn't once seen Penny since the pregnancy was known.

'Yes. She does. Soon.'

So - it was out in the open. He faced the decision like the prospect of a new and unknown job, his body empty, uncertain. 'A quiet one, then?'

She nodded. 'A quiet wedding.'

There seemed little else to say. As he edged past the hallstand to the cheap coloured-glass mosaic of the front door his eyes noted, without taking in, the black leather of the studded jacket suspended there. Only the polished half-globe with which he'd rapped for admittance, spotlighted the sudden reversal in his feelings about Penny. Cold as brass.

Had he looked up more quickly to the flurry of a lace curtain in the bedroom window, he would have glimpsed two faces. One male and unknown; in the other he might have recognised his future wife.

'There will be a proper wedding. But the bride cannot wear white.'

'But Penny doesn't want that, Grandmother. They want a quiet wedding.'

'I understand that we – that is to say, your Grandfather and I – are paying for this wedding. In the absence of any father on the bride's side.'

'We can't force a wedding on them that they don't want, Gran.'

At the familiar mode of address Nancy blenched. 'I would like my friends and acquaintances to be present.'

Peter paused. Almost all of them would be dead now, surely? But in her imagined social sphere they lived on. *For a thousand years in Thy sight are but as yesterday, seeing that is gone like a watch in the night.*

'What about the registry office ceremony – Red Thomas'll be best man - and then a service in church when it's not news any more, when the spotlight's off us and people take the marriage for granted?'

Nancy pondered. The putty-coloured strings of her neck alone carried the hint of shock. 'To which my friends could be invited?'

For a second he wanted to shout, *It's our wedding, you meddling old snob, not yours. Choosing the guests is our business.* But to what purpose? Modern reality and his grandmother shared no common ground.

The dead had no visiting cards.

But this time, to his amazement, Nancy relented. Weariness had won the day where reason failed. She raised a languid handkerchief like smelling salts to her face.

'Very well,' she said. 'If that's what you prefer.'

So his fate was sealed at the Wormley Row Registry Office. And then six months to the day: the morning haze promised equatorial heat. After calling a taxi at sunrise and helping Penny up the hospital steps Peter was directed to a small cell-like room to wait until summoned.

Another young man sat opposite, not speaking, pulling at cigarette after cigarette like a piglet voracious at its mother's teats. When the placebo of nicotine failed he stood and stamped up and down, whey-faced, until the upheaval inside him became too much and he rushed into the small adjacent lavatory to vomit. Peter checked himself for qualms. No, nothing noticeable. What was the fuss all about?

'Mr Munnerly?'

A diminutive nurse showed him into the maternity ward. Under a single sheet Penny lay sweating, attached in some way to a machine whose dial displayed the flickerings of a hyperactive needle. For a moment she smiled, then resumed her frown of concentration, preoccupied with the eruption to come.

The knoll of her belly summoned phantasmagoric images: a Russian doll with another, identical doll inside, an igloo buried under snow. But a nurse who stood anxiously watching the machine dispelled fantasy. When a young man in white coat, presumably a doctor, came in, they conferred in agitated mumbles.

'I'm afraid you'll have to leave,' she said.

Restored to the waiting cell, he kept the door open. Minutes passed; the hands of his watch crept round their track. After what might have been forty minutes – but in truth he'd no idea of time's crawl – he got up, angry and impatient, and tiptoed to the maternity ward door. Silently, with infinite care, he eased it a fraction open.

To watch unobserved brought visceral excitement. Pictures blossomed: an old-style football overinflated, the bladder forcing itself through a gap in the leather; the extrusion of a pate, its quiff of hair wet and dark as an oil-slick; an earthquake groaning, the entrails of the earth excreting.

He found himself moved. Tears greased his face, a thin uncontrollable glycerine that welled up without will or spring. He wasn't weeping from sorrow or joy or any known emotion, as if the turbulence rose from some limb or organ he didn't possess, had never possessed. And yet the tears flowed.

'Does that child never stop crying?'

'No. Yes. Joni's teething. Look - I thought you might like to read this. I thought you'd be pleased that I've started writing as well.'

Lodged since his marriage in two spare rooms at Havana House, it had still taken Peter a certain courage to approach his mother. Only a suppressed longing for her approval made him take the step.

'I'm very pleased. Read it out to me.'

'It's a bit long. A whole novel.'

'What's it about?' While she spoke, Margery examined sundry unpromising garments that lay spread out on her sofa: Peter remembered she had a literary soiree that evening. 'Not a romance, I hope?'

'Well no, not exactly. But I think it could make some real money. It's historical.'

He'd researched the events surrounding his hero Burlington's adventures with assiduity. Before she could object further he began to read, louder than was strictly necessary: *Across the icy plain of Balaclava the enemy outnumbered the British by twenty to one. But nothing could daunt Horatio*

Burlington or dampen his indomitable valour. For him the day would bring either victory or death.. Er…it's based on real events. I've read lots of books about the period.'

At once he regretted the last sentence. But he need not have worried. Already his mother's attention had strayed far away from his literary endeavours.

'I'm told you've been having rows with Penny.'

If only she'd listen. He could even remember the closing lines: *With a silent snip of the cutters Burlington parted the barbed wire strands. In a moment he was crouching low under the veranda where the enemy officers sipped their drinks. Burlington's agile mind translated their harsh, sinister words with ease.*

If *only* Margery would listen. 'Can we can talk about Penny another time?'

'We can, indeed. At the moment -' Margery held up a beaded frock from a previous age and sighed, 'Moths! Yes… tell me… later.'

You won't have read any of my father's other short stories. No one but me has, though they're rather good. Nothing like the dreadful Burlington sagas - I suspect poor Great Uncle Ralph's life, among others, was pressed into service as plot line for one of them. Captain Henry would've been for it next, had he lived. (My father, I mean). They seem to have sold in their thousands, though. Where the money went is anybody's guess.

I like to think my father might have been a fine writer if he hadn't been born a Munnerly. I like to think if he'd got the chance to write his own death this is how he'd have done it.

The End of the Line

They parked the car and followed the narrow road towards the ravine.

'This is it,' Peter said. 'Llewellyn's Leap, they call it. Where the Welsh chief, fleeing from his enemies, took a flying leap, right the way across.'

'He can't have.' The woman - Dilys, she was called, a pick-up, blonde, well preserved, tubbyish - wasn't impressed. You had to be careful with smartypants like this one. Sharp-tongued, he'd discovered - late. 'It's too wide.'

Peter surveyed the gorge. Sixty feet below, water gathered in a deep black pool before pouring down towards the North Welsh coast with its far glimpse of Liverpool's towers speckling the sea-mist. Above the pool, the single-lane road writhed across an iron bridge crowded with people. 'It's just a legend,' he said. Clutching for extenuation, he added, 'The battle was real, though.'

'Who was he fighting?'

Peter cleared his throat. 'Dunno. Some enemy.'

'But who were they?'

'English, probably. After the battle of –' His tongue faltered, unsteadied by the two double whiskies he'd had for lunch. What did it matter? 'Way back. Edward, wasn't it? Or thereabouts.'

'You don't seem very sure.'

'I'm not. It's not my period. Burlington's more British Empire. Look,' his voice took on an edge, 'I've got to go and get harnessed. You stay here and watch. Enjoy it.' He stooped and pecked her on the rouged cheek. Never go too fast with this sort.

'You sure you really want to? Above all that?'

'Yeah, no problem. I'm not scared.'

He'd always wanted to do it, bungee jumping. Partly, it was to prove his courage, to prove he'd always had more guts than most men. A pity his daughter Joni couldn't be here to witness it - to be proud of her old.... but of course though there was always the other thing, the thing about wanting to strip to the waist in front of a crowd of women and show off his muscular body – still pretty good if he held his belly in. It was only after he'd invited Dilys to the event and couldn't get out of it without loss of face that he realised you made the jump fully clothed. The water below was no more than a safety net if things went wrong. Which they wouldn't.

There was no queue for harnessing. Not many people fancied a free fall, more a topple than a jump, so that you plunged straight down without slewing around. Not many people had the bottle for that. They didn't get the kick.

He wondered if the organisers picked the right rope for the jumpers' weights, as they'd done once for a hanging. While a pair of grinning helpers attached it at ankles and trunk, he avoided their eyes, his heart pounding. He felt a faint stir in his bowels and checked his belly against risk of accidents. In a way it helped, it took your mind off the jump.

But there was a pleasurable tremor in watching the skinny kid before him climb over the handrail to the ledge, then, with arms clasped across his chest and his back towards the drop, plunge like a falling matchstick. The spectacle had an unreality, even something of the humour of an animated film. At the low point of the fall there was an element of surprise in the bounce and rebound and then the way the kid, with a kind of joggling motion and a whoop of delight shared by the onlookers, went into a second, lesser fall. After that, the upside-down dangle, the slow haul back to the bridge and the jubilant (plain) girlfriend. It was all over in five minutes.

The need for action calmed. As with everything, the waiting was worst. At least it would win his bet with Red Thomas. A hundred quid, if he paid. Worth it for that alone, never mind Dilys.

'Okay, go ahead.'

Peter climbed onto the ledge. He breathed deeply. Keeping his body straight as instructed, he leaned back. For an instant he felt fear, electrifying fear - but it was doused by the knowledge that there was nothing he could do. Wonderful! Then the void of falling, with no time to think, the up-rush of trees, bridge, water as he twirled and turned, then straightened out, the rope beginning to tighten, to decelerate. At the expected yet still startling rebound he rose only halfway back to the bridge but the rope jumped higher still, snaking into a loop that fell into the precise shape of a noose about his neck. He raised his hands to grip it, to loosen it, but it was no use, he couldn't throw it off.

There were shouts. He was sure he heard Dilys scream. 'His neck! God! Stop him! For God's sa-a-k-ke!'

But by the time he was hauled in, there was no breath in the man whose last sight had encompassed, beyond river and hills, the city that had been his family's livelihood and the theatre of their separate lives.

My poor father never did get his hands on Havana House. Great Aunt Flo died only a few months ago now, taking the last of the skeletons in the Munnerlys' custom-built Gillows' cupboard (made with the finest Cuban mahogany) to her grave.

And I went and sold The House in Rock Park - or at least the wreck of it - and started writing this.

"Finished!" I called out, late last night.

There was no answer. Just as I deserved - I bet I've been a pain since I started on the old clan history.

So there was no one in to say, Way to go, Joni!

No one to ask me, So - are you going to publish it?

Mmm... Good question.

I mean, the Munnerlys, well they rose and fell with the city across the water. Just a typical Liverpool family you might say.

Maybe not. Here's another good question. If they were your family, would you?

I've made up my mind about one thing. That painting, the one that started it all? I'll be telling them to keep it.

J.M. 2009

The kitchen-wing to the rear of Havana House during demolition 2008.

Havana House 1941

A dying man's fancy: even in those dreadful days, who could refuse it?

He moved forward and looked up at the Munnerlys from the low position his wheelchair offered. These late Victorian portraits were very like the photographs he had made his living from – constrained, tight, careful and absolutely rooted in their time. James Bartholomew scanned the work and thought about how he might have done it differently with more experience. He would have lost the classical allusions for a start, *and* the maritime background… he hadn't done too badly with the girls, though, whose upturned faces still shone against their black ringlets. Alice seemed especially radiant today… from this angle. And he could see already the signs of what would be his abiding fascination with light and dark - but not much else that he recognised or wanted to be remembered for.

From conversations with James Bartholomew's great niece, Mary Bartholomew, some time after this book was completed.